SELECTED BOOKS BY L. S. B. LEAKEY

(and published by Schenkman Publishing Co.)

WHITE AFRICAN: An Early Autobiography

KENYA: Contrasts and Problems

(forthcoming)

ADAM, OR APE: A Sourcebook of
Discoveries about Early Man

UNVEILING
MAN'S ORIGINS

Charles Darwin in 1881.

UNVEILING MAN'S ORIGINS

TEN DECADES OF THOUGHT ABOUT HUMAN EVOLUTION

By

L. S. B. LEAKEY

AND

VANNE MORRIS GOODALL

SCHENKMAN PUBLISHING COMPANY, INC.
Cambridge, Massachusetts

Library of Congress Catalog Card #68-24269

Copyright © 1969
SCHENKMAN PUBLISHING COMPANY, INC.
Cambridge, Massachusetts 02138

PRINTED IN THE UNITED STATES OF AMERICA

Contents

LIST OF PICTURES

Acknowledgements

Courtesy of the American Museum of Natural History:
Pictures on pages II, XVIII, 2, 20, 28, 193-198.
Courtesy of the National Geographic Society:
Pictures on pages XII, 168, 170, 199.
Courtesy of the British Museum of Natural History:
Picture on page 200.

Errata:

Page 21 for *Plaeocene,* read *Paleocene* in Table
Page 30 for *Cromagnon,* read *European Upper Palaeolithic*
Page 61, in the picture caption, for *likely,* read *possible*
Page 168, in the picture caption, for *Tobias* read *Norman Mitton*

PREFACE

Since 1960 I have given numerous lectures in the United States of America, both to students at Universities and also to students at Junior Colleges and to a lesser extent at High Schools, right across the country. Over this period I became more and more aware of the lack of a suitable book to provide the background for students of anthropology concerned with the wide, overall, gradual growth of our knowledge of human evolution.

It was, therefore, with great interest, that I listened to a proposal of Mr. Alfred S. Schenkman of Schenkman Publishing Company that I write such a book. Specifically, he suggested that it be aimed primarily at college students of anthropology but also that it be a book which would appeal to the ever-growing circle of laymen interested in the origins of man.

The proposal intrigued me greatly. But I knew that if I took on such a project it would involve an incredibly vast amount of detailed research, in a number of libraries; and I knew also that I simply could not spare the time for this work although I recognized its importance. I suggested therefore that I should search for a suitable collaborator who would undertake that vitally important task of reading up on the literature and selecting from it the information to be included in our book. I accordingly approached Vanne Morris Goodall.

Mrs. Goodall has long been interested in anthropological literature. She is known as a writer, and is the mother of Jane van Lawick Goodall who has become famous for her studies of wild chimpanzees. After some hesitation, Mrs. Goodall agreed to accept the assignment and in fact is responsible for the actual writing of Chapters I–XII.

The task was a very difficult one, for two reasons. Clearly, a great deal of the information available had to be omitted. Furthermore, it was equally clear that the decade-per-chapter device would make it impossible to produce a book of this particular nature with successive chapters flowing freely, one to the next. Indeed, each chapter in Part II is meant to be read as a distinct entity although each should be read in its proper sequence.

I am sure that despite what drawbacks this book may have, the majority of my colleagues will find that it fills a real gap in the available information on early man. Having already had the typescript read by a number of non-specialist friends, Mrs. Goodall and I firmly believe that many laymen who are interested in the story of man's origins and in how that story has gradually been unfolded will read this book with very real interest.

L. S. B. LEAKEY

February, 1969
NAIROBI, KENYA

INTRODUCTION

It was in 1859 that Charles Darwin startled the English-speaking world by publishing his first book dealing with what was then the "Theory of Evolution." A few years later, he brought out his second book — a little less than one hundred years ago — in which he discussed the descent of man.

Darwin proposed the idea that man, as we know him to-day, was a member of the zoological family which includes apes, monkeys and prosimians, and he went further, and prophesied that the day would come when it would be shown that Africa had been the main evolutionary center of all the old-world higher primates, as well as of man himself.

During the long period of nearly one hundred years that has elapsed, gradually and slowly some of the facts concerning our own evolution have been uncovered and become easier to understand; but we are still a very long way from knowing all that we need to know about ourselves and our evolutionary history.

From time to time, as for example after the discovery of the Java skull at the end of the last century, people have thought that the story was complete. It seemed, then, that a clear "missing link" between ape and man had been found, and the complexity of the true story was not even faintly appreciated.

Before and just after World War I, a considerable number of human anatomists postulated, on theoretical grounds, that man must have separated from his nearest cousins, the great apes, at least as far back as the separation of the Families to which the dog, the cat, the hyena and the bear belong. This was a rational view, but when little or no evidence in support of it came to light, there was a change of scientific opinion, so that in many textbooks published since World War II it has been suggested that man's evolution was by four simple stages (or as the French call them "stades évolutives"). Each in turn, according to these suggestions, succeeded the other, during the last five or six million years.

This book is not intended to be a detailed study of the basic facts concerning human evolution; that could not be provided, adequately, in fewer than three or four volumes. Its aim, rather, is to give the serious student of man's evolution some background concerning the many changes of opinion, and the setting up and discarding of theories, which have taken place over the years, especially since Darwin.

In the main chapters we shall discuss the facts which were uncovered during successive decades and also the effect those facts had upon the thinking of the time. In the final chapter we deal with the decade which is not yet complete, beginning in 1960.

It is of remarkable significance that during this current decade the prophesies of Darwin and the postulations of men like Sir Arthur Keith, Sir Grafton Elliot Smith and Professor Boule have been vindicated. Much remains to be done. There is every hope, as travel across the continents of the world becomes easier, as finance for research becomes more available, that the next decade will see an even greater acceleration of knowledge about our past.

In recent years, a great deal of research has been concentrated upon Africa and Asia, but there is undoubtedly a very great deal still waiting to be discovered in Europe. We should also consider the Americas within the orbit of our study; since large mammals were crossing from Asia into North America, across the land bridge where we now find the Bering Straits, it would seem highly improbable that man would not have followed.

The authors may not live to see the day but they are prepared to prophesy that within thirty to forty years from now, evidence will have been found to show that some form of manlike creature (possibly *Homo erectus*) reached the Americas from Asia at least 300,000 years ago.

To conclude this Introduction, it is necessary to say a little about the format of the book and the reasons why it has been written.

The aim has been to provide the story of the major discoveries which have been made and the attitude of the world at large to those discoveries during the ten decades since Darwin published his first book dealing with the theory of evolution.

The book thus falls into two parts. The first provides a background of events which have a bearing on the topics of this book up to the year 1859. The second part is in ten successive chapters, each of which covers one decade. Inevitably, there is a certain amount of repetition between one chapter and another because these chapters are not intended to be read as a consecutive story. Each chapter, rather, summarises the events of the decade with which it is concerned and the reactions during that decade. Finally comes a very brief Epilogue pointing to the vast amount of research that remains to be done and highlighting some of the principal problems facing prehistorians.

While the book is primarily intended for college students, we hope that it will also prove of interest to a much wider public. Increasingly, laymen and even students in high school, want the background against which modern discoveries (which are now being made so rapidly) can be assessed.

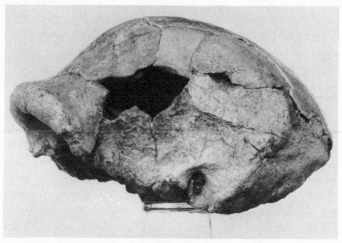

An African "Pithecanthropine,"
Homo erectus, from site LLK, Bed II, Olduvai.

NOTES ON CERTAIN TERMS
USED IN THIS VOLUME

1 — BED In certain geological contexts, the term "Bed," written with a capital B, is used for an associated group of strata with certain structural and/or faunal elements in common, and regarded as representing an identifiable unit. Thus the strata at Olduvai Gorge, in Tanzania, were sub-divided by Reck into Bed I (at the bottom), through Beds II, III, and IV, to Bed V which lies uncomformably on the other deposits, at the top of the sequence.

2 — BRECCIA The word breccia means the broken-up fragments of stone, often mixed with other material, such as soil and rubble, filling an old cave or fissure. Very commonly, a breccia is hard, having been cemented together with lime. At certain sites, cave breccias have been found to contain contemporary bones and teeth, and sometimes artifacts.

3 — CHURCH The word Church used in the context of this book and written with a capital C, refers to the Christian Church in the broadest sense of the word irrespective of sect.

4 — FAMILY Family spelt with a capital F is the word which is used by zoologists to link together groups that are not as closely related to each other, as are the species of a single genus, but which are, neverthe-

less, closer to each other than to the members of another Family. For example: the Family Felidae includes both living and extinct "cats," in the widest sense. For example: lions, tigers, leopards, pumas, jaguars, domestic cats and many extinct cats are all generally known as Felidae. They are clearly closer to each other than to any of those genera or species which are members of the Family Canidae, which includes dogs, wolves, jackals, foxes, etc. The Family Hominidae links together not only the species of the genus *Homo,* or man, but also related creatures such as the "near-men" or Australopithecine, and such proto-hominids as *Ramapithecus* and *Kenyapithecus.* In contrast, the living and extinct great apes are separated from the Family of the Hominidae and fall into a Family of their own named Pongidae.

5 — GENUS The word genus (plural genera, adjective generic) is the word used to group together members of different species which stand close to each other but are sufficiently distinct to be classified as separate species. For example: the horse, the donkey and the zebra are clearly more closely related to each other than they are to cattle. They are ranked as members of the single genus *Equus,* although each of the three qualify as different species, namely, *Equus caballus, Equus asinus,* and *Equus zebra.*

6 — HOMO and HOMINIDAE The word *Homo* is the scientific name for the genus of man, and includes the species *sapiens,* which is man as we know him

today, and other species such as *erectus* and *habilis*. Many other species names, in this genus, have been proposed from time to time (such as *heidelbergensis* and *neanderthalensis*) but these are not now generally recognized. Derived from the word *Homo* is the Family name Hominidae, (see notes on Family above). The adjective hominid implies membership of the Family Hominidae.

7 — MATRIX   In a geological context, the word *matrix* means a mass of material (either homogenous or otherwise) in which are found specimens which are as it were "foreign bodies" of the mass.   These are usually fossil bones or artifacts.   A matrix is usually a hardened deposit, cemented by lime or some other similar substance, but it may be soft like clay or loess.

8 — PONGIDAE   This is the scientific name for the Family of the living and extinct great apes, (see Notes on Family above).

9 — TORUS   The word *torus* is the scientific term for a bony ridge.   Although it can be applied to a ridge on other parts of the skull and on the mandible, the most common use is in connection with the massive brow ridges situated above the eye-sockets in the great apes and some types of fossil man such as *Homo erectus* and Neanderthal man.

10 — VILLAFRANCHIAN   This is the term used today to refer to the basal part of the Pleistocene geological time period, in Europe and Africa.   The word derives from the fossil site of Villafranche.

The "Villafranchian" was only recognized as part of the Pleistocene in 1948. Until that time, the beginning of the Pleistocene was usually regarded as coinciding with the onset of the first glacial episode in Europe i.e. Gunz. Today, deposits which were once termed Lower Pleistocene are regarded as representing the early stages of the Middle Pleistocene.

II — GENERAL NOTE

THE DIVISION OF THE STONE AGE. In the earlier days of Prehistory, the stone age was divided into Palaeolithic or Old Stone Age, and Neolithic or New Stone Age.

After a time, it became clear that the Palaeolithic spanned a very long period of time and it was divided into Lower Palaeolithic, Middle Palaeolithic, and Upper Palaeolithic. Each of these three cultural divisions corresponded roughly to the then accepted time divisions of the Lower Pleistocene, Middle Pleistocene, and Upper Pleistocene.

Subsequently, the term Eolithic was introduced for some supposedly primitive stone age cultures that were thought to date back to the Pliocene. This term has been generally abandoned and the earliest known cultures such as the Oldowan, from the lowest levels of Olduvai Gorge, are now grouped with the Lower Palaeolithic.

After a time, following discoveries at Mas d'Azil, a transitional cultural division was introduced between the Upper Palaeolithic and Neolithic and termed Mesolithic, meaning Middle Stone Age. This must not be confused with the term "Middle Stone Age" as used in South African studies of prehistory where "Middle Stone Age" is roughly the equivalent of the Upper Palaeolithic of Europe.

NOTE ON THE TIME DIVISIONS.

In this book we are not concerned with geological time prior to the age of "Mammals." The age of mammals is divided into Paleocene, Eocene, Oligocene, Miocene, Pliocene, Pleistocene and Recent.

There have been revolutionary changes in our concept of the time covered by these divisions. For instance, in the early 1900's the Miocene was thought to have been about 4 to 3 million years ago and is now believed to span from 25 to 10 million years ago. Similarly, the start of the Pleistocene was once put at circa 500,000 but is now placed at 3 million.

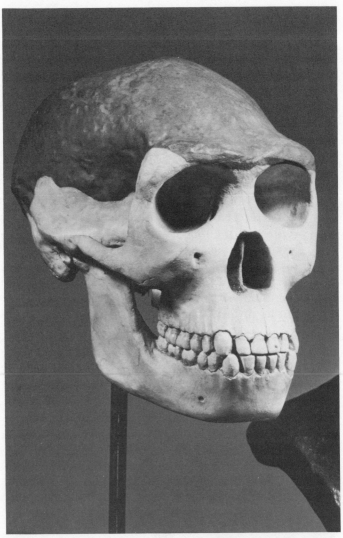

Java man, *Homo (Pithecanthropus) erectus*. Restoration of the skull of Java man by McGregor. Note the low receding forehead and prominent brow ridges. Although commonly regarded as a type ancestral to *Homo sapiens*, Leakey does not accept this.

PART I

THE BACKGROUND

Excavations such as this in France during last century laid the foundations of prehistory. Today more precise methods would be employed. But this early pioneering work established that man was living during the Ice Age.

CHAPTER I

PRELUDE TO THE SCIENCE OF PREHISTORY

Prehistory is a comparatively new branch of science but the records of man's preoccupation with the enigma of his origins go back to the dawn of history. In his early search for the truth man drew upon the riches of his imagination. Strange stories, which were invented to explain the mystery of creation, can be found in the myths and legends of many peoples.

As the centuries passed, however, man began to look for a rational explanation of the mystery of life through the study of nature. About 53 B.C., Titus Lucretius Carus, one of the great Roman poets, published his philosophic poem *De Rerum Natura* (On Nature), which is now claimed as one of the masterpieces of literature. Amongst the many brilliant theories he postulated was one which astonishingly anticipates the theory of evolution with which Charles Darwin electrified the world more than eighteen centuries later.

This famous account of the origin of life and the development of the human species was subsequently regarded by the Christian Church as being incompatible with the Old Testament account of the traditional Hebrew belief in the special creation of Adam. For nearly nineteen hun-

3

dred years therefore, in all communities where the powerful influence of the Church was exerted, such views as those expressed by Lucretius were fanatically opposed and suppressed. This led ultimately, as we shall see, to a bitter conflict between the Church and the pioneers of the science of prehistory, which began in the eighteenth century and was brought to a climax by the publication of Darwin's *Origin of Species* in 1859. But meanwhile, wherever there were men who were consumed by the desire for knowledge, scientific data steadily accumulated.

On looking back through the ages, it is surprising to find how often the significance of such data escaped recognition until it was pinpointed by the bright light of genius. The making of tools was for a long time regarded as one of the things which clearly differentiated man from all other animals. Recently this idea has been more sharply defined as "the making of cutting tools" since some other creatures do, in fact, make simple tools of perishable materials. The crude stone cutting tools which were made by our very early ancestors are now accepted as the clues from which we learn about their cultural life. For many thousands of years however, these implements, fashioned from flint, chert, obsidian, or other types of stone, lay scattered over the face of the earth and were regarded as mere "curiosities of nature." Some Greek philosophers believed that these had been launched by Zeus and called them "thunderbolts," and local superstition in many countries invested them with magical powers. (This is still the case in many primitive communities today.)

It was not until the latter part of the sixteenth century

that Michael Mercati, physician to Pope Clement VIII, realized the true significance of these so-called "thunderbolts." "Most men," he wrote "believe that *ceraunia* (thunderbolts) are produced by lightning. Those who study history consider that they have been broken off from very hard flints by a violent blow in the days before iron was employed for the follies of war." He then went on to quote the verses from *De Rerum Natura* written by Lucretius in 53 B.C. His views were not acceptable to the public opinion of his times, however, and it was more than a hundred years before his writings were published.

Towards the close of the seventeenth century, a London apothecary, John Conyers, who was described by his friend John Bagford as a man "who made it his chief business to collect such Antiquities as were daily found in and about London," discovered "the Body of an Elephant." Not far away he came upon a pear-shaped stone. The two friends must have examined and discussed this stone on many occasions, for Bagford wrote later that "he came to know it well." In his opinion, which must have been met with a good deal of scepticism at the time, it represented "a British weapon made of a Flint Lance like unto the Head of a Spear," which had been used in the days before Britons knew the use of brass or iron. Bagford suggested, therefore, that the elephant was one of the many which had been brought to England during the Roman occupation of Great Britain, and had possibly been slain with the stone weapon discovered by his friend Conyers.

Man finds it difficult to adjust his mind to evidence which does not fit in with preconceived ideas, and Bagford's remarkable interpretation of Conyer's discovery created little impression on his contemporaries.

It was nearly a century before John Frere of England made the next correctly interpreted and recorded discovery of man-made "stone tools." These stones described by Frere as "spear-heads," were found in the brick-earths filling an ancient valley at Hoxne in the County of Suffolk, England, and were associated with the bones of extinct animals. Laying aside the preconceived ideas of his generation, Frere had the courage to announce what he believed to be the true significance of his discovery. In 1800 he described his finds in *Archaeologia*. "These implements," he wrote, "belong to a very remote period indeed, much more remote in time than that of the present world." He had not only recognized the human origin of the tools, but suggested that they belonged to a very remote geological period, an idea which was incompatible with the persistent and widespread belief in a universal flood in Noah's time. This brilliant interpretation, however, was ignored by contemporary scientific opinion. It was not until 1859, when the brick-earths of Hoxne were revisited, by the geologist Sir John Evans and by Sir Joseph Prestwich, that Frere's interpretations were verified and his place as one of the pioneers of prehistory was established for all time.

Other scientists in the eighteenth century reached similar conclusions. Several papers were published in the early part of the century which claimed that *ceraunia* were, in fact, stone tools made by early man and compared them with those currently in use by members of primitive tribes, particularly those of the American Indians. The old belief that stone tools were "thunderbolts" was gradually abandoned and scientists began to accept them as cultural evidence of early man.

The concept of man as a primitive being using crude stone tools, however, was violently opposed by the Christian Church, which unequivocally accepted the Old Testament account of the Creation. In this we are told that there was a special creation of each individual species of animal, and finally of man who was made in the image of God. Clearly, then, for all who believed in the word-by-word accuracy of the English translation of the Old Testament story, any suggestion that a primitive creature who used stone tools could have been ancestral to Adam was not only abhorrent but heretical.

It was not long before another vitally important step was taken towards the unveiling of man's origins, when the true status of fossils (which had puzzled generations of men) was finally established. Fossils are now known to be the remains of plants, shells, and bones which have been preserved by natural means in the earth's crust, and altered in constitution according to the influences to which they have been subjected. They are of vital importance to the prehistorian for they supply the clues which he needs for the reconstruction of the long procession of diverse creatures which have lived on our planet. Just as the stone tools made by early man lay on or beneath the surface of the earth for many thousands of years without being recognized for what they were, so too the true nature and meaning of fossils was not appreciated until comparatively recently.

From time to time history records the strange suggestions which were put forward to explain the enigma of the fossil. Some wondered if they were perhaps germs, or if they had generated from seeds or from the rocks. A more fanciful theory suggested that they had fallen fully fashioned from the skies. In the sixteenth century, the immortal Leonardo da Vinci, who might well be regarded as the pioneer of Palaeontology, realized the significance of fossils. But his views were far in advance of his time and were suppressed, since they were in direct opposition to those held by the Church.

Two centuries later, the advanced thinkers of the eighteenth century came to believe, as Leonardo had done, that fossils were of organic origin. The next step towards a better understanding of their true value was to find out when the fossilized creatures they represented had lived. It was only natural, in an age which was deeply influenced by religious doctrines, that enlightenment should be sought in the Old Testament account of the creation. An answer which was acceptable to a very large number of scientists was found in the story of "The Flood;" this suggested that all creatures, except those saved by Noah at God's command, had perished under the waters of a "universal deluge." Clearly, then, it seemed highly reasonable to accept the idea that fossils were the remains of those creatures which had been drowned in the Flood and buried under the debris which covered the earth when the waters went down. This became known as the "Diluvial theory" and was strongly supported by the Church.

But there were a great many free-thinkers who believed

that this philosophy was contradicted by the evidence of geology. Groups of fossilized animals, each differing from the others, had been observed in successive geological strata, indicating clearly that they had lived at different geological periods of time. If this was so, then they could not all have been drowned in one and the same great flood.

In order to accommodate the new data, the famous French palaeontologist Baron Georges Cuvier, who had made a prolonged study of fossils, suggested that there had been a succession of catastrophes, each followed by an era of calm during which the earth had been restocked. He was careful, however, to fit this new philosophy into the accepted biblical chronology. God's first creation, he suggested, had consisted mainly of marine creatures, his second of reptiles and his third chiefly of mammals. These were destroyed in turn and a fourth creation, as described in the Old Testament, was ultimately swept away by "The Flood," with the exception of the inmates of the ark. Thus the Church was still able to maintain that the only remains which could be regarded as of human origin were those found in or near the Euphrates valley in which Adam and his descendants had lived, and where Noah had built and stocked the ark with animals.

Launched by a man of such reputation as Cuvier, the new "Catastrophic theory" gained immediate support; but a handful of advanced and courageous thinkers began to suspect that the duration of geological time had been grossly under-estimated. At this time the Church was still blindly supporting the conclusion proposed by Archbishop James Ussher in 1593, that the world had been created in

4004 B.C. He had arrived at this estimate by computing first the ages of Adam and his descendants, as recorded in the Old Testament and then by adding a number of years deduced from a study of Hebrew history. Cuvier could not possibly fit three additional creations into this time scale. He therefore adopted the proposals of Comte Georges de Buffon, a great French geologist, and pushed the creation of the world back by 80,000 years.

This sudden growth of rational thought in Europe during the latter part of the eighteenth century, hampered as it was by the orthodox beliefs of the Christian Church, paved the way for the establishment of the science of prehistory and a gradual and awe-inspiring extension of the geological periods of time.

Leonardo da Vinci

10

CHAPTER II
1800—1859

The early part of the nineteenth century was remarkable for the intense interest which scientists in Europe, England and America began to take in cave exploration. Limestone caverns attracted particular attention because the drip from a limestone roof forms a stalagmite covering for the floor and thus seals in the cave's history. Reports circulating in 1822 claimed that the caves in southern Germany had yielded the remains of many extinct forms of animals, including those of elephant, rhinoceros, hyena and bear. The news of these discoveries inspired an English clergyman, Dean William Buckland, at that time also Reader of Geology in the University of Oxford, to investigate the Paviland cave on the Welsh coast. It was not long before Buckland made one of the notable discoveries of the century.

The Paviland cave is set in a limestone cliff and soon yielded a store of prehistoric treasures. Flint implements, as well as ornaments and tools of bone and ivory, lay embedded with the same species of extinct animal which had been found in the stratified caves of Germany. With them Dean Buckland discovered a human skeleton, stained with red ochre. This became known to science as "The Red Lady of Paviland," though it was later found to be that of a young man. The problem of interpreting his discovery placed the Dean in a difficult position. As a geologist, he suspected that he had found the remains of an Old Stone Age man. As a Christian minister and a Diluvialist, the tenets of his faith precluded him from admitting it. In the end, he apparently allowed his conscience to dictate his pronouncement. He explained his discovery by suggesting that although the remains of the animals had probably been swept into the Paviland cave by flood waters, the human body must have been intrusively buried at a much later date, when man had settled in England long after "The Flood."

A few years later a Roman Catholic priest, the Reverend John MacEnery, began to investigate the huge rambling limestone cave on the Devon coast of England known as Kent's Cavern. He found man-made stone tools in association with the same species of extinct animals that Dean Buckland had uncovered in the Paviland cave; but unlike the Dean he did not allow his scientific judgment to be obscured by religious beliefs. In spite of the severe criticisms to which he was subjected by the Church, and even by Buckland, Father MacEnery remained convinced that he had found sufficient evidence to maintain that man had lived in England long before the time of the "Biblical Flood," as a contemporary of the extinct animals whose remains he had found. The notebooks in which he recorded his discoveries and interpretations were found and published many years after his death.

Meanwhile, the extensive limestone caves near Liège, in

12

Belgium, had been attracting the attention of an intrepid and dedicated palaeontologist. In the course of his explorations, Dr. Schmerling of Belgium investigated more than forty caves along the banks of the River Meuse and collected quantities of fossilized animal remains which were associated with implements of stone and bone. Human fossil remains were both fragmentary and scarce, but since he found them embedded in the same strata, Schmerling maintained, in spite of opposition, that all three groups were contemporary.

In 1833 he made the discovery for which he is famous. Day after day, month after month, he had been visiting a cave named Engis. In order to reach its heart, he had to be let down a steep cliff by rope and then crawl on all fours along a subterranean passage. Standing for hours, often with his feet in water or mud, he superintended the breaking of the stalagmite crust to penetrate the breccia beneath. His reward came at last with the discovery of an almost complete "primate" skull. It was embedded five feet within the breccia and surrounded by the remains of extinct forms of elephant, bear, tiger, hyena, rhinoceros, reindeer and other animals which had disappeared before the beginning of what was then accepted as the time boundary of the late Stone Age. In Schmerling's opinion, this was conclusive proof that man had been living in Europe "long before the Deluge."

The scientific world was not ready to accept his verdict. The great English geologist, Sir Charles Lyell, visited Liège and examined the skull. On looking back it seems strange, today, that a man of Lyell's brilliance, a man who

13

had begun to measure the geological age of the world in millions, instead of in thousands, of years, should have been so sceptical about the age of the Engis skull. His conscience, however, which allowed him to accept a very great antiquity for the world itself did not permit him to believe in the existence of man at the remote period to which Schmerling had assigned the skull from Engis.

Another discovery that was totally ignored during this period was made in 1848 in Gibraltar. The minutes of the Gibraltar Scientific Society record that a human skull was found in March of that year in Forbes Quarry on the north face of "The Rock." This well-preserved skull was eventually brought to England in 1862, but it was not until the beginning of the twentieth century that its unique place in the history of human evolution was finally established. It represented, as we shall discover, the first recorded remains of Neanderthal Man, whose history plays an important part in the story of man's evolution.

Geologists had, by now, accumulated a vast wealth of data in support of the idea that the history of man stretched back beyond the boundaries which had been laid down for it by the Church; but this idea was still not given an official blessing either by science or by the Church. It was largely due to the brilliant and indefatigable work of a Frenchman, M. Boucher de Perthes, that the balance of scientific thought was finally tipped in favour of those who believed in the existence of "antediluvian man."

Boucher de Perthes was a man of infinite patience, good humour and courage, a lover of antiquities as well as a great scholar. In 1825, when he was about forty years old, he was appointed to the post of Customs Officer at Abbé-ville on the river Somme. The gravel beds in the valley of the Somme were continually being exploited for commercial purposes and had already been investigated and found to contain the fossil remains of extinct animals. These gravel beds naturally attracted the attention of Boucher de Perthes, who soon began to notice that many curiously shaped stones were dug from the gravel by the workmen. In spite of the fact that the gravel beds had been assigned to the so-called prediluvial geological period, Boucher de Perthes was convinced that the stones, which he began to collect from the workmen, were in fact "stone tools" which had been made by man. A less courageous man might have been daunted by the scorn and ridicule with which his interpretation was greeted on all sides. Boucher de Perthes remained convinced that he had found positive proof of man's existence in Europe before "The Flood."

In 1846 he published his now famous book, *Antiquités Celtiques et Antediluviennes,* in which he claimed that the soils outside Abbéville contained stones worked by "antediluvial man," in association with the fossil remains of large animals belonging to extinct species. His book was hotly criticized, and Boucher de Perthes began to be regarded by scientists as a dreamer and a visionary. The Church dubbed him a heretic. He does not appear to have had one single supporter of any authority until 1854, when he was visited by a Dr. Rigollot, a physician from Amiens, whose scepticism about the age and authenticity of the "stone tools" from Abbéville was well known. Having examined the Abbéville stone implements, Rigollot returned to Amiens and discovered that there were similar stones in comparable strata at St. Acheul, near Amiens. Completely converted, Rigollot ranged himself enthusiastically on the side of the opponents of the diluvialist theory, and it is fitting that the work of these two pioneers of prehistory should be associated with two early cultures of the Stone Age known as the Chellean (or Abbevillian as it is now called), and the Acheulean.*

In 1859 two English geologists, Sir Joseph Prestwich and Dr. Hugh Falconer, visited Boucher de Perthes at Abbeville. Both were convinced that his claim to have discovered man-made tools in association with the remains of extinct animals which had lived in a remote geological period was fully justified. Falconer was well known for his work on the extinct animals which had been found in the Siwalik Hills of India. Prestwich was a distinguished scientist, also with an established reputation. On his return to London, Prestwich read a paper to the Royal Society in which he stressed the immense importance of these discoveries in the gravel beds at Abbeville, and expressed the view that he had been "greatly astonished to find that all, if not quite all, of the animals whose bones are found in the same beds as the axes, are extinct." Sir Joseph's opinion carried great weight in scientific circles and this meeting of the Royal Society marked the beginning of a gradual conversion of opinion to the views which Boucher de Perthes had so courageously maintained in the face of so much ridicule and opposition.

---

* Chellean after the site at Chelles, Abbévillian after the site at Abbéville and Acheulean after St. Acheules.

As we follow the gradual unfolding of the vast panorama of prehistoric times, we shall find that prehistory owes many of its major discoveries to the hand of chance. Over and over again we shall see how the fossil remains of animals and man have been exposed by parties of workmen who have been excavating for building operations, mining for metals or precious stones, or digging out quarries for commercial purposes. Sometimes, however, it is the forces of nature cutting through the earth's crust which reveal the layers of gravel and sand or clay and other deposits which have been laid down, one upon the other, through the long passage of geological time. In either case, chance does no more than provide the opportunity of acquiring knowledge. The remains which workmen have brought to light, the secrets of the past which lie buried in the exposed strata of valley and gorge, are of no value to the prehistorian unless their significance is recognized and their story translated by experts.

We have already seen how the significance of a fossil human skull, found in a quarry in Gibraltar in 1848, went unrecognized. Nine years later, some workmen quarrying the limestone cliffs of a deep ravine near Düsseldorf in Germany made a similar remarkable discovery. The celebrated Neanderthal cave (which has long since been demolished), then opened half way up the steep side of the cliff and, in 1857, the remains of a strange individual were found buried beneath its floor. By good fortune, a medical doctor, who was interested in fossils, recovered the remains of this skeleton from the workmen and sent them to an expert anatomist for examination. The extraordinary char-

17

acter of the skull presented many problems. These were made the more difficult and unhelpful because no other animal remains and no artifacts were found nearby. There was literally no associated clue to guide the scientists in their estimation of the antiquity of these human bones.

The find aroused intense interest in scientific circles. Lyell travelled to Germany to make a study of the geology of the terrain in which it was found and took a cast of the skull back to England where he gave it to Thomas Huxley to study. After completing his analysis of its characters, Huxley came to the conclusion that, in spite of its exceptionally apelike features, it was in fact the skull of an extreme variant of modern man.

In his paper on Neanderthal man, which was published in 1873, Huxley wrote, "The Neanderthal cranium has certainly not undergone compression and in reply to the suggestion that the skull is that of an idiot, it may be urged that the *onus probandi* lies with those who adopt the hypothesis. Idiocy is compatible with very various forms and capacities of the cranium, but I know of none which present the least resemblance to the Neanderthal skull; and furthermore I shall proceed to show that the latter manifests an extreme degree of a stage of degradation exhibited as a natural condition by the crania of certain races of mankind."

It is to Professor William King of Queens College, Galway in Ireland that honour is due for being the first scientist to recognize that the skull cap from the Neanderthal cave belonged to a representative of a hitherto unrecognized type of mankind. Although the vault of the skull was

18

the only well-preserved part of the fossil, King created a new species for its reception and named it *Homo neanderthalensis*. Scientists of the time were not prepared to accept King's view because they were not then ready to believe that the prehistoric world might have been peopled by different species of mankind. Many of them therefore continued to regard the Neanderthal skull as a pathological specimen. More than half a century was to elapse before King's opinion was endorsed by science and the famous skull from the Neanderthal cave accepted as representing a member of the species he had named *Homo neanderthalensis*.

The first half of the century was now almost over, and the stage was set for one of the most dramatic moments in the history of science. Lyell and other geologists of the period had pushed the story of our planet back in time, presenting mankind with a new and awe-inspiring concept of a world which was old beyond imagining. Their research had revealed that great areas of land, now submerged by water, had once joined Asia to America, Europe to Africa, and Great Britain to the rest of Europe, so that in prehistoric times both men and animals could have wandered across these land bridges from one continent to another. Evidence had also been discovered to show that large parts of the world had once been frozen in the grip of a great glacial epoch.

In Switzerland, between two glacial deposits, geologists had found a bed of fossilized plants which could only have flourished in a temperate climate. This, together with an accumulation of additional data, led them to believe that there must have been both glacial and interglacial stages within the Great Ice Age. The history of the world was now divided up as shown in the accompanying list of geological divisions of time.

From about 1850 on, the "Diluvial" theory rapidly lost ground. Not only was it untenable in the light of the new geological data which was coming to hand, but many scientists were beginning to wonder whether the Biblical "flood" had, in fact, been a "Universal Deluge," or merely a local flood confined to the area in and around the Euphrates Valley, where Adam and all his descendants, including Noah, had reputedly lived.

Charles Lyell

GEOLOGICAL DIVISION OF TIME
AS ESTABLISHED AROUND 1850

Quaternary
{
Holocene or Recent
Pleistocene
}

Tertiary
{
Pliocene
Miocene
Oligocene
Eocene
Plaeocene
}

Secondary
{
Cretaceous
Jurassic
Triassic
}

Primary
{
Permian
Carboniferous
Devonian
Silurian
Ordovician
Cambrian
Pre-Cambrian
}

Learned men throughout the ages have speculated upon the number and combination of species which Noah must have packed into his Ark. In the sixteenth century the famous Elizabethan sailor and explorer, Sir Walter Raleigh, calculated that there must have been "eighty-nine distinct species of beastes," but by the end of the eighteenth century this figure had been doubled, and the estimated proportions of the Ark had grown correspondingly formidable.

The problem was aggravated by evidence which had now come from such far-flung areas as Africa, Asia, America and Europe, that each continent had its own particular fauna. Forms ancestral to these animals had been found in geological deposits formed before the Biblical "Flood" could have taken place. Only by means of a miracle therefore, could Noah have collected individuals from all the living species in the world before the "Flood" and redistributed them afterwards.

The controversy regarding the existence of man in Europe before the "Flood" now began to die away, and scientists concerned themselves with the chronology of glacial and interglacial man and his cultural remains. Now that the true significance of stone tools was appreciated, a vast wealth of data was beginning to accumulate about the social life and industries of our remote ancestors. A succession of classified cultures known as Stone Age, Bronze Age and finally Iron Age had by now been established.

Theories and ideas, suppressed for so long by religious prejudice, now struggled into the light, and were apparent in the new and rational approach which was being adopted in the search for man's origins. Many of the old beliefs which had been exaggerated by poetic fiction were therefore swept away. Wherever the curiosity of man led him to investigate and chronicle the marvels of the natural world, scientists now found themselves in the possession of a vast storehouse of knowledge. It remained for someone to postulate a theory which would account for the diversity of life on earth and the ultimate miracle of mankind.

The idea of evolving life, which was so soon to capture the imagination of man, was not a new one. Until now, however, it had been stultified by the bigoted acceptance of the dogma of special creation, which maintained that all species remained exactly as they were when first created. A handful of advanced thinkers of the late eighteenth century, such as Carl Linnaeus, the famous Swedish naturalist, Erasmus Darwin of England, and Chevalier de Lamarck of France, had put forward revolutionary ideas which were in opposition to the theory of immutability of species. It was, however, Charles Robert Darwin who finally gave the world a new concept of the animal kingdom.

Charles Darwin was born at the turn of the century, in 1809. He was the grandson of Erasmus Darwin, the famous English naturalist whose theories foreshadowed those which were to make the name Darwin one of the most famous in the history of the world. Charles Darwin was destined by his parents for a medical career, but his obsessive interest in natural history was always his guiding star. In 1831, while still a student at Cambridge University, he was persuaded to join a scientific expedition bound for the South Seas. The mind of the young Darwin who set sail in 1831 in *H.M.S. Beagle* was still strongly influenced by the doctrine of "Special Creation" and the consequent immutability of all forms of animal and plant life. The very numerous marvels of nature which he observed and duly recorded during the voyage gradually led him to formulate his entirely different theory to account for the multiplicity of species and their origins.

As the *Beagle* cruised among the Galapagos Islands off the South American coast, Darwin watched and wondered. "The whole of my pleasure," he wrote, "was derived from what passed in my mind while admiring the views by myself, travelling across the wild deserts or glorious forests . . . accumulating facts in silence and solitude." He noticed how the birds and reptiles of each of the islands that the vessel visited, while clearly resembling the forms of South America, nevertheless varied from one island to the next. He was struck, moreover, by the resemblances between the giant fossil forms of such creatures as the armadillo and its smaller modern counterpart, and by the fact that both were only to be found in South America.

He saw how living creatures, though apparently closely allied to each other, exhibited variations even in different localities within the same general area. He became more and more convinced, as his data accumulated, that the theory of the immutability of species was wholly untenable. Species were not constant. They were continually being modified. The important questions were "how" and "why?" Could it be the case that such a creature as the giant extinct armadillo was ancestral to the existing one, or were both of them extremes having the same origins?

Darwin returned to England with an astonishing number of meticulously recorded notes on the plants and the living creatures he had seen on his travels. The voyage lasted five whole years and has been immortalized by Darwin in his book *The Voyage of the Beagle*, published in 1839.

From 1839 onwards Darwin's health, which had been excellent before the voyage of the *Beagle*, began to deteriorate. It was never to recover. He made a supremely happy marriage to Emma Wedgwood; he had no financial worries and he was a devoted father to his children; but the illnesses from which he suffered interrupted his work and were a perpetual handicap.

Darwin worked for twenty years on the material he had collected, and formulated his Theory of Evolution. He worked, too, on the many experiments in breeding by means of which he substantiated his theories. In spite of physical difficulties, he drove himself relentlessly, and his many publications demonstrate the number and diversity of his interests. The titles of his papers include such subjects as "Power of Movement in Plants," "Climbing Plants," "Fertilization of Orchids," "The Expression of the Emotions in Men and Animals," "Insectivorous Plants," and many more were the subjects which interested him.

In June 1858, twenty-seven years after the *Beagle* had set sail for the South Seas, Darwin, who was still not ready to publish his book on the origin of species, received a letter from a certain Alfred Russel Wallace. Wallace, who was to become one of England's highly respected scientists, was then a young man "collecting" in the Malay States. In his letter to Darwin he enclosed an essay on the "Theory of

Evolution." Darwin was aghast. "I never saw a more striking coincidence," he wrote to a friend. "If Wallace had my manuscript sketch written out in 1842 he could not have made a better short abstract."

The situation presented a difficult ethical problem, which was finally solved by Darwin's friends, who persuaded him that a preliminary outline of both theories should be published simultaneously. These papers made little stir in the scientific world and it was not until Darwin's book *The Origin of Species by Means of Natural Selection, or the Preservation of Favoured Races in the Struggle for Life,* was published in 1859 that the storm broke.

Briefly, Darwin's theory of evolution, which was in direct opposition to the doctrine of "Special Creation," was based on the belief that all species are mutable and can trace their ancestry back to the lowliest forms of life. Darwinism, as it came to be called in scientific circles, further maintained that variations in all living organisms can arise spontaneously and that these variations may be advantageous or otherwise.

The organism developing the variations which are most advantageous to its particular environment will survive and reproduce the species; those less favoured will tend to die out in the fierce struggle for existence and become extinct. Nature can therefore be said to select those breeding qualities which safeguard the future of the species and to favour, by natural selection, the survival of the fittest.

Darwin frequently acknowledged that he had been inspired and influenced by the work of his friend and colleague Lyell. In *The Principles of Geology,* 1830, Lyell estimated the various geological periods in terms of millions of years, rather than in the hundreds which his predecessors had allowed. Only such a vast geological concept of the antiquity of the world could have accommodated the slow and gradual processes of evolution which Darwin described in the *Origin of Species*. Today Darwin's concept of evolution is so well known and so widely accepted that it is difficult to imagine the magnitude of the sensation it caused when it was published in 1859. The first edition of the book was sold out very quickly and the reaction to its doctrines was immediate.

The Church saw it as a threat to the very foundations on which the doctrine of "Special Creation" and the literal belief in Biblical chronology had been built. It therefore attacked Darwin with an almost fanatical intensity. The idea that a wise and powerful God had designed and created all living things in a permanent immutable form, was part of the Christian faith. Many scientists therefore, while recognizing the genius of a theory which would withstand the most acid tests of logic, nevertheless turned from the idea of the mutability of species on purely religious grounds.

Darwin himself was emotionally involved in the conflict which his theory of evolution had provoked, and he always stressed that he had not been motivated by any anti-theological bias when he wrote the *Origin of Species*. For those who came to accept Darwin's theory, man began to be regarded as the ultimate triumph of a process of evolution which was even more miraculous and awe-inspiring than was the concept of a special creation of each separate form of life.

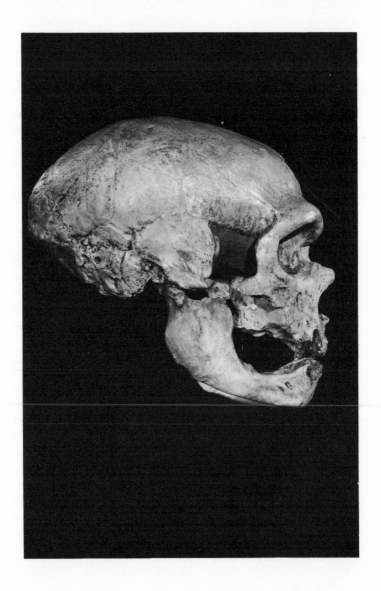

A "classic" Neanderthal skull (this one from La Chapelle-aux-Saints) of the type first discovered in 1848 in Gibraltar. It exhibits the long low narrow skull, heavy jutting brows and large face common to European Neanderthalers.

PART II

THE TEN DECADES

Cromagnon cave paintings; the running boar from Altamira, Spain and the bull, horses and stags from Lascaux cave, France.

CHAPTER III
1860—1869

The first important find in this decade, and one which proved to be of a highly controversial nature, was made by M. Edouard Lartet in southern France. Lartet was trained as a lawyer, but a deep-rooted interest in antiquities, fostered by many fossil discoveries in the grounds of his estate, induced him to abandon his profession in order to study osteology and geology. This decision was of inestimable value to science. The important discoveries he made in the field, which helped to mould the scientific opinion of his times, and the valuable contribution he made to the creation of the science of human palaeontology, have earned him a place as one of the greatest of the early pioneers of prehistory. Lartet was one of the freethinkers of his age — a man whose scientific judgments were not obscured by prejudice, and who on many occasions reacted against the "Diluvialists" and those who believed in the "Catastrophic" theory.

Like many of his contemporaries, he became obsessed with the current enthusiasm for cave exploration. In 1860, during a visit to the Haute Garonne district of France, he investigated a cave which had been found near the village of Aurignac by a stone mason. Chance had sent this workman up to a hole in the side of a hill, in which he thought he had seen the kind of stone he needed for his road repairs. To his surprise, the "stone" proved to be a human bone. On digging further into the hole, he came upon a large stone slab; when this was removed he found himself inside a cave. It was almost entirely filled with the bones of human skeletons.

Unfortunately for science, the mayor of the neighboring town heard of the discovery and ordered the remains to be taken from the cave and given a Christian burial. When Lartet arrived to investigate the strange and exciting discovery, no one would tell him where these valuable anthropological relics of the past had been interred. He began, therefore to make a systematic exploration deeper into the cave. Below the level of the floor he found evidence of a much earlier occupation. The remains of man and his artifacts, together with bones and teeth of the extinct animals with which he had shared his world, lay buried beneath the breccia.

The human remains were too fragmentary for Lartet to find out much about their physical development, but he learned much about their way of life from the other material which he uncovered. Outside the cave a small terrace concealed the existence of one of those rubbish accumulations, or "kitchen middens" as they came to be called, which have told prehistorians so much about the people responsible for them. As Lartet sifted and sorted the objects which had accumulated in this deposit, he brought to light the remains of extinct animals such as cave bear, cave lion, mammoth and woolly rhinoceros, as well as bison, elk and reindeer. Many of the bones which he found had been broken open and charred. Clearly these primitive ancestors of man already knew how to make fire. They had not simply existed side by side with the now extinct animals, but had hunted them for food, breaking open the bones to obtain the marrow. From a study of the combined geological, archaeological and palaeontological evidence, Lartet decided that he had conclusive proof of man's existence in the prediluvian times.

Another exciting aspect of the story, but one which became evident only at a later date, was the discovery that the necklaces of shells and bones, and the worked bone and stone tools found at Aurignac, were fashioned in the same style as those found in the Engis cave in Belgium as well as the Paviland cave in England.

The finds at Aurignac convinced many, including the influential and highly respected geologist, Lyell, that man had lived on the Earth for a far longer period than had previously been estimated. In 1863 Lyell published his views in *The Geological Evidence of the Antiquity of Man*. This book, which was to become a landmark in the literature on prehistory, clearly indicated Lyell's conversion to a belief in very early man, and helped to swell the ranks of those who were beginning to support the new concept of man's antiquity.

Early in 1863, another notable event took place in France, in the Somme valley, near Abbeville. Boucher de Perthes was now an old man and his claim to have found man-made stone tools in association with extinct fauna was beginning to be accepted by the majority of scientists. His cherished ambition to find the remains of the men who had made the tools, however, remained unfulfilled. The workmen he was in touch with had been offered substantial rewards for any human remains they might find in the gravels, but in spite of all their efforts not a single trace had been discovered. On 23rd March, 1863, however, as work was proceeding in the Moulin Quignon pit, one of the workmen noticed an object in a stratum of black sand and gravel. Boucher de Perthes was sent for and took it from the matrix himself. It proved to be a human tooth. His long-sought prize had come to light, at last. A trench was dug and a few days later, with what must have been a feeling of overwhelming excitement, Boucher de Perthes found a human jaw in the deposit.

The Moulin Quignon pit had already yielded many stone tools of the Acheulean and Chellean type, so that Boucher de Perthes announced that he had recovered a human fossil in association with ancient stone tools. News of the discovery spread quickly and brought scientists from France and England to see the remains of what was claimed to be the first example of a "river-drift" or "terrace-gravel" man dating to Palaeolithic times.

Very soon, however, it began to be rumored that some at least of the so-called "Stone Age implements" from the Moulin Quignon site were forgeries which had been planted by the workmen. It was not long, therefore, before the authenticity of the tooth and jawbone also began to be suspected. A conference to discuss the matter was held in Paris in May, 1863 and when it finally broke up opinions were still divided. Boucher de Perthes, strongly supported by his French colleagues, continued to maintain that the jaw belonged to a representative of Palaeolithic man; while the English claimed that it was a forgery. Boucher de Perthes at this stage allowed his precious fossil to be cut in half and its contents analyzed. Even this drastic measure, which revealed that the bone was surprisingly fresh and still contained 8 per cent of animal matter, did not shake the opinion of the French scientists.

The general consensus of English opinion was expressed by Sir John Evans, whose word carried great weight in scientific circles. In a letter to the *Athenaeum* that year, he stressed that the controversy over the Moulin Quignon jaw should not be allowed to obscure the real significance of the work done by Boucher de Perthes in the Somme valley. Despite whatever forgeries had been, or might still be, perpetuated by the workmen employed on the sites, he maintained that "the main facts of the case remained unaltered and unassailable." "Flint implements, undisputedly the work of man," he wrote, "have been discovered . . . in conjunction with the remains . . . of extinct mammals in undisturbed fluviatile gravels . . . under circumstances which prove that those beds were deposited at an epoch, to the minds of most people inconceivably remote, and long before the surface of the country had received its present configuration."

Evans now expressed the hope that the Moulin Quignon jaw might be consigned to oblivion. He added the reminder that "the existence of counterfeits presupposes the existence of genuine originals." The faith of the French authorities, however, in the authenticity of the Moulin

Quignon jaw, apparently remained unshaken until the end of the nineteenth century, when it ceased to be listed as a fossil representing early man. The episode which thus ended so tragically for Boucher de Perthes came to be regarded as a valuable warning to scientists not to accept such evidence at its face value.

It is also interesting to note that Sir Arthur Keith, who later examined a cast of the mandible, recorded this view in the *Antiquity of Man* (1925) : "Time will probably show that the pioneer of Abbéville was not only right about the human implements of the terraces but also about the human remains."

Prehistorians were now on the threshold of a startling disclosure which was to throw light on a moving and unsuspected facet of the cultural life of our primitive ancestors. This discovery, too, was made in France. During the course of his cave explorations in the Dordogne country, and along the lower slopes of the Pyrenees, Lartet had already found numerous primitive carvings, hundreds of reindeer antlers engraved with drawings of other animals and other examples of primitive art. But the discovery which was to be linked forever with his name was made in 1864 in the cave of La Madeleine. Work had been in progress there for some time when Lartet arrived one day with the British palaeontologist Hugh Falconer. Lartet's workmen presented him with five pieces of a thin plate of ivory. When the fragments had been fitted together, the two scientists found that the intricate pattern of shallow lines which had been engraved on the ivory represented the head and body of an elephant, covered with the long, flowing hair characteristic of the mammoth or extinct elephant of the glacial period. This was indeed a discovery of major importance. The little engraving, executed so long ago and preserved for posterity in the French cave, proved beyond any doubt that primitive man had lived and hunted animals long since extinct and had made accurate drawings of them during the Glacial Age.

Grave doubts had been expressed about the great age of the many previous discoveries of art figurines and engravings. It had been suggested that they had been executed at a much later date than that proposed for the bones of the animals that had been used as drawing surfaces. This engraved mammoth however, could not have been drawn by hunters visiting the cave in a postglacial period. The animal represented was clearly one which had adapted itself to the cold, and was associated with the retreating ice sheets. It must, therefore, have been the work of an artist who had actually seen a great woolly mammoth alive — a man who had lived in the glacial age and been sufficiently advanced in the cultural sense to make recognizable drawings of the animals around him.

Writing about Lartet's famous discovery in his book that discussed the antiquity of man, Lyell stated that in the light of such clear proof of palaeolithic man's intelligence, it seemed probable, after all, that he had advanced "sufficiently to burn or bury his dead, or even to have a belief in a future state." When Sir Charles used the word "palaeolithic" to describe early stone age man he was using the new name given to the "Old Stone Age" by Sir John Lubbock. In 1865, this eminent English archaeologist (afterwards Lord Avebury) had published an important book. In *Prehistoric Times,* Lubbock recognized and named two subdivisions of the Stone Age: the Old Stone Age became the Palaeolithic, and the New Age was henceforth known as the Neolithic.

By this time, Lartet, and his colleague M. Christy, had explored some ten of the now famous rock shelters and caves in the Dordogne country in France. Among these, the caves of La Madeleine and Le Moustier have become the type sites for the cultures to which they gave their names: the Magdelenian and Mousterian. Scientists who visited the Dordogne at the time were of the opinion that the Le Moustier site was the most ancient of all those investigated by Lartet. No objects of worked bone were found in the cave deposits. All the implements were made of unpolished stone; many of them were only trimmed on one side. This became known as one of the main characteristics of the Mousterian culture, in contrast to the Chellean and Acheulean.

The cave at La Madeleine, unlike Le Moustier, had yielded not only the engraving of the woolly mammoth on the ivory plate, but also a rich collection of tools and weapons of bone antler and ivory. Many of these had been decorated with the vigour and artistry which has since come to be associated with the loveliest of all the cultures of our remote ancestors — that of the Magdalenian.

Lartet, at this stage, proposed a classification of the period represented by his finds in the Dordogne country. It was based on the succession of the dominant forms of animal life that he had brought to light from stratified geological deposits, and he included the following subdivisions: (1) the Age of the Aurochs, or Bison; (2) the Age of the Woolly Mammoth and Rhinoceros; (3) the Age of the Reindeer; and (4) the Age of the Cave Bear. Since the reindeer predominated throughout the series, Lartet named this prehistoric period the Reindeer Age.

In 1866, M. Edouard Dupont, a distinguished Belgian geologist, made a discovery which caused a sensation in scientific circles. With the aid of a grant from the Belgian government, he was exploring a series of limestone caves in the valley of the River Lesse, when he found a manlike lower jaw in Trou de la Naulette. Its geological age was clearly established from the beginning, for it lay embedded in an undisturbed stratum fourteen feet below the floor of the cave and it was accompanied by the remains of "Mid-Pleistocene" fauna, including the mammoth, rhinoceros, cave bear and reindeer.

The teeth of the Naulette mandible were presumed to have dropped from it after death, and only the front region and the left part of the body of the jaw remained. Famous scientists of the day who studied this specimen, were impressed by its great strength and its many morphological peculiarities which included a marked absence of chin. As anatomists of the time maintained that the projection of the chin is an essentially human character, they regarded the Naulette mandible as being "directly interposed between the jaw of an anthropoid ape and a modern human being." This view was reiterated several years later by M. P. Broca. "The jaw from La Naulette," he wrote, "is the first evidence to provide the Darwinians with an anatomical argument. It is the first link in the chain which, according to them, ought to lead from man to monkeys."

The Naulette mandible, which became almost as famous as the skull cap from Neanderthal, was eventually preserved for posterity in the Royal Natural History Museum of Brussels. It was to be many years before its real nature was recognized and it was established as an authentic relic of the Neanderthal type.

The search for the origins of man in France during this decade was not confined solely to cave exploration. In 1865 two French antiquarians, M. Ferry and M. Arcelin, began to investigate the open country near the little village of Solutré. The area covered by their search was about two acres of land. Below the Upper Palaeolithic strata, which had been disturbed, the explorers found evidence of a new culture, which has since taken its name from the site. It is characterized by stone tools which are shaped like "laurel leaves." Below this "Solutrean" stratum, at a depth of about ten feet, was an Aurignacian occupation layer. The Solutrean level became known as the "equine layer," because wherever exploratory trenches were dug the fossilized remains of horses were found, most of which had been broken up and charred by fire. It seemed as though wild horse flesh must have been a favourite form of diet of these people. It was reckoned that the hunters and their families must have eaten at least 10,000 horses on this site alone!

The associated tools of worked ivory, bone and stone found in this layer, as well as the remains of the extinct animals, were similar to those which were found at other sites. In an even older stratum, evidence of the Mousterian culture was discovered, but although the two anti-quarians continued their search for many seasons they were not fortunate enough to find any identifiable remains of fossil man. They had, however, produced sufficient evidence to demonstrate that early man sometimes set up his home in open country during the periods (possibly the summer months) when the climate was warm enough for him to abandon his caves and rock shelters.

In 1868, Louis Lartet, the son of Edouard, made another momentous discovery in the Dordogne country. This time it was the result of the building of a railway line along the beautiful Vézère valley. The line cut through an ancient rock shelter and exposed the prehistoric treasures which lay embedded in the strata.

Inside the cave, in the upper level, in association with the same species of extinct animals and the same type of culture as his father had found in the cave at Aurignac, Louis Lartet discovered the skeletons of five individuals. The find was a rich one for the prehistorians, for the remains included the skulls and bones of an old man, two adult men, a woman and an unborn infant. These were undoubtedly representatives of the people responsible for the Aurignacian culture. Examination of the bones revealed that the skulls were massive and the leg bones relatively long in comparison with the short upper arm bones. These proportions were likened to those of the tall, slender present day Sikhs of the Punjab. Anthropologists came to the conclusion that these remains should be regarded as proto-types of a new fossil race of man, to be known as the Cromagnon.

The story of early man was at last beginning to take shape. It was becoming increasingly clear that the successive cultures of man, like the civilizations of recorded history, had followed each other as one phase of man's development closed and another began. The problem now to be faced was, how they were to be distinguished when found alone. This having been achieved, the order of their succession must also be established.

The difficulties which had to be overcome were thus sharpened, because so many of the discoveries made in the early days of prehistory were taken out of the matrix in which they had been embedded, by enthusiastic amateurs. They were then placed in museums without the necessary data to help those who sought to interpret them.

Chance plays an important part in the finding of the fossils, but it is the combined expert skills of the trained interpreters who measure their value for science. The anatomist or palaeontologist reconstructs the creatures represented by the fossil remains. The archaeologist studies the accumulation of associated artifacts left by man in order to build a picture of his daily life and cultural pursuits. The geologist reads the story of the matrix in which the remains were found, and fills in the geological background of the world at the time.

All the discoveries of early man that we have examined so far, were made on the Continent of Europe, with the exception of the "Red Lady" from the Paviland cave in South Wales. This does not, however, mean that work was not in progress in other parts of the world. In England and in North and South America, enthusiastic prehistorians were vigorously searching for the origins of man. The most controversial discovery made in North America was the "Calaveras skull," which was found by some gold miners in California in 1866. It was examined by many scientists, who finally decided against its antiquity, since they concluded it closely resembled the skulls of the modern American Indians of the neighborhood.

In Brazil, a labyrinth of limestone caves was investigated by a Dutch naturalist, Dr. Lund. After nine years of work he accumulated a vast quantity of the remains of extinct species of animals, which he had found in association with the fragmentary remains of man and innumerable artifacts. He finally brought to light a human skull which convinced him that man had lived in Brazil "before the historic period," but his views were not shared by the anthropologists who examined it. In their view, it so closely resembled the skulls of the modern American Indians that their interest in Lund's discoveries waned. It was widely believed that no race had preceded the American Indians in the New World.

CHAPTER IV
1870—1879

In 1870, eleven years after the *Origin of Species* had shaken the foundations of man's belief in the special creation, Darwin published another book, *The Descent of Man and Selection in Relation to Sex*. This met with the same violent reactions as his earlier work, and passed through what he called the same "fiery ordeal" as the *Origin of Species*.

The world found the book profoundly shocking. For centuries man had been flattered and uplifted by his conviction that he had been "specially created" by God and endowed from very beginning with all the physical and mental attributes of modern man. Darwin, however, maintained that although man had "risen to the summit of the organic scale, and had developed a god-like intellect, he still bears in his bodily frame the indelible stamp of his lowly origin." The vast majority of thinkers of that time were revolted by the new and horrifying idea that they had developed from some lowly pre-existing form, and by their own growing suspicion that Darwin might be right.

Anticipating the bitterness which his theories would arouse, Darwin sought to mollify his readers in advance. In the concluding chapters of his *Descent of Man* he wrote "He who has seen a savage in his native land, will not feel

44

much shame if forced to acknowledge that the blood of some more humble creature flows in his veins." He preferred to think that he was related to the little monkey who saved its keeper from a dreaded enemy than to the savage who delighted in torturing and mutilating his fellows. In any case, whether man himself liked it or not, Darwin was convinced that we are descended from the Old World or Catarrhine monkey stock.

Every aspect of this logical sequel to the *Origin of Species* was hotly debated, and the book loosed a flood of ideas from the many scientists who sought to establish man's place in nature in the light of the new knowledge. It should never be forgotten that Darwin wrote this great, classic work on the evolution of man at a time when there was very little fossil evidence to support his theories. One by one, the major discoveries made by prehistorians since then have confirmed his conclusions.

The theory which he postulated about the birthplace of man has, in the last few years, been most strongly supported by new evidence. From a study of available data, Darwin pointed out that the living mammals of any specific area were closely related to the fossilized remains of extinct species which had been discovered there. He concluded, therefore, that since the two living primates most closely resembling man — the chimpanzee and the gorilla — are both to be found in Africa, it would be reasonable to suppose that man's birthplace would eventually be discovered on the African continent.

Biologists who set out in 1870 to find out where and when man diverged from the Catarrhine monkey stock expected to conduct a comparatively straightforward search. They were convinced and remained so for many years, that diligence and patience would eventually bring to light a succession of evolving forms, each more primitive than the last. This chain was to lead them by a single strand from modern man right back to the most 'primitive' form of all and so at length to the so-called 'missing-link,' the intermediate form between man and the apes. Most anatomists were agreed that man is physically constructed on much the same general pattern as the other mammals, and they had classified him as belonging to one of the Families within the Order Primates. As the idea that man was descended from some primitive stock began to take root, this classification was again discussed, and detailed comparisons began to be drawn up between man and the apes.

In his book, *Evidence as to Man's Place in Nature,* Thomas Huxley stressed the importance of making detailed studies of the dentition of men and apes. He pointed out that the Old World primates (all except lemurs) have thirty-two teeth, the same as in man, but that the New World monkeys found on the American continent have thirty-six. Thus the New World monkeys differ more from the Old World apes, than the latter do from man. In fact, Huxley went further and claimed that in every visible character man differs less from the higher apes than these do from the lower members of the same order of Primates.

While still discussing and investigating the structural similarities between man and ape, scientists now began to turn their attention to another vital and engrossing problem. If man had evolved from some lowly form, how and

46

at what period of his evolution had he developed those powers of intellect and moral consciousness which set him apart from all other animals on earth? On the anatomical level, the capacity of man's brain in relation to the brains of other animals was exhaustively investigated and assessed. In the final analysis, most scientists believed that the real explanation of man's superiority could not be accounted for by anatomical measurements alone. "What," they asked, "was the major difference between man and the animals?" The most popular answer was "man's belief in God." Darwin, however, maintained that this could not be considered an innate distinction, since it was "a state of being" which only became apparent in man after he had undergone a period of culture.

Philosophers, naturalists, geologists and other scientists all sought to isolate the elusive quality which distinguishes man from the other animals, and which has given him the mastery of the world. But analysis of man only revealed more and more how closely he resembled the other mammals. It was not difficult to produce unquestionable proof of the fact that they, like man, clearly demonstrate their ability to feel shame and sorrow, hatred and love; or that each of them like man, exhibits identifiable, individual traits.

Many of these discussions turned ultimately upon what an English Archbishop, Dr. Sumner, termed man's "capacity for progressive and improvable reason." This, in turn, raised the problem of discovering how to establish the point at which "reason" can be separated from "instinct." There were, of course, many who clung to their belief in a "special creation," and bitterly attacked Darwin's theory of transmutation. Some of his critics maintained that if it were true that man had descended from some primitive, ape-like form, it was more than likely that the fossil remains of this intermediate link which led from ape to man would by this time have been discovered by geologists.

Replying to this criticism, Lyell pointed out that the search for man's origins had scarcely begun. Vast areas of the world's surface, in particular those lands which the geologists calculated were the most likely to yield fossil remains of man and ape, awaited scientific investigation. The sciences of prehistory and palaeontology were in their infancy and the lack of fossil evidence, he held, should not be allowed to influence the judgments of those who had not yet accepted the theory of evolution.

Turning to the discoveries of this decade, we find once again that it is France which makes the major contribution to the study of man's past. First came a discovery on the beautiful Côte d'Azur just above the road which runs along the coastline between Nice and Mentone, where the red rocks of Grimaldi rise from the blue Mediterranean sea. Here in 1872, Dr. Paul Rivière, a French scientist who was working in the district, brought to light a human skeleton in one of the caves that riddle these cliffs. It was stained with red ochre and surrounded with fauna and cultural objects similar to those which Edouard Lartet had found in the cave of Aurignac. He was convinced that he had discovered another representative of the Cromagnon race, and that the position of the remains, when found, indicated that this early man had been given a form of burial.

Some of his colleagues shared his view. Rivière removed the skeleton with infinite care, and sent it to the Jardin des Plantes in Paris, where it came to be known as "The Famous Man of Mentone."

Between 1872 and 1875 Rivière dug up five more skeletons in the Grimaldi caves, two of which were children. The cave in which they were found was explored more thoroughly at a later date, as we shall see in the next chapter, and eventually became known as the Grotte des Enfants.

These finds in the Grimaldi caves represented the major discoveries of this decade. At the same time, however, fragments of human remains were continually being brought to light in many parts of the world, as well as extinct species of animals and the artifacts which early man left behind him.

In South America, the work of a remarkable naturalist was beginning to startle the scientific world. In 1873 Florentino Ameghino, later to become Dr. Ameghino and Director of the National Museum at Buenos Aires, discovered the skeleton of a woman and the fragmentary remains of another individual near the little town of Mercedes. All the bones were in a state of considerable disintegration, but Ameghino decided that the deposits in which he had found them belonged to the "Pliocene period." He was convinced that he had found the "Fossil Man of Argentina."

Anatomists who examined the remains were of the opinion that they did not differ greatly from the bones of representatives of modern American Indian tribes. Geologists who visited the site near Mercedes refused to believe that the stratum in which the remains had been discovered was older than the "Pleistocene period." Ameghino remained convinced. As no remains of Tertiary man had been brought to light anywhere else in the world, he concluded that "since man must have had a beginning somewhere, his place of origin and centre of dispersal were in the southern portion of South America." As time passed, this theory became so firmly fixed in his mind that he constructed a complex genealogical tree of the human race, by which he claimed he could trace man's descent from a species of small monkey found in the lower Tertiary strata of Patagonia. Having done this, he then set to work to discover evidence in support of his theories.

Ameghino's work aroused a storm of criticism, especially in later years, from such eminent scientists as Dr. Aleš Hrdlička of North America, and many of his innumerable discoveries were discredited. It came to be generally considered that he had greatly exaggerated the antiquity of his finds, and that none of them had given the scientific world any grounds whatsoever for affirming the existence of fossil man, either in South or North America.

CHAPTER V
1880—1889

Twenty years after Edouard Dupont had found the famous Naulette mandible, another significant discovery was made in Belgium. The explorers this time were a party which set out from Liège University in 1886 under the leadership of three distinguished Belgian geologists, Julian Fraipont, Max Lohest and Marcel de Puydt. They went to a limestone cave known as the Grotte de Spy on the eastern side of a little valley a few miles from the town of Namur. Here they began to investigate the terrace deposits which sloped downwards from the mouth of the cave to the stream level in the valley below. Their excavations passed through two different strata, each yielding evidence of an ancient human occupation, and then reached a third and very shallow deposit. Here, lying on what had once been the hearth of a prehistoric people, they discovered the remains of two human skeletons. This exciting find was supported from the outset by the fully documented scientific evidence which was necessary to establish its importance and age. All the clues to this particular prehistoric puzzle were unearthed in the presence of the expert in charge of the work. The geological age of the discovery was easily determined, for the skeletons were accompanied by Palaeolithic stone tools and what was at that time regarded as a Mid-Pleis-tocene fauna. This included the remains of woolly rhino-ceros, woolly mammoth, cave bear and cave hyena — all cold climate animals.

The fossil human bones were well preserved and easy to study. They included two brain cases, two lower jaws, parts of both faces, as well as some of the long bones of the skele-tons. When comparative studies were carried out it became apparent that the two skulls from Spy exhibited the same flattened brain cases, receding foreheads, and huge brow ridges as those which had distinguished the skull found in the Neanderthal cave in 1857. Following that famous dis-covery many fragmentary fossil remains, such as those found at Brux in 1872, or at Schipka in 1883, had been claimed as the remains of man of the Neanderthal type. In each case, however, the claim had not been fully established owing to lack of associated scientific data. All the finds made during the excavations at Spy were, on the contrary, fully authenticated and scientists felt justified therefore, in claiming that the two skeletons represented the primitive species of man, named in 1864 by Professor King and hence-forth to be known as *Homo neanderthalensis.*

Anatomical studies of this extinct type of man were now made by several distinguished scientists, revealing a mixture of both modern and so-called primitive characters. From measurements of the brain capacity it was estimated that Neanderthal man had stood halfway between the lowest and the highest of the then known human extremes, and was certainly far above any ape maximum. The average height of the body was estimated at about five feet, while some suggested from the structure of the knee joint that this species was "unlikely to have attained a fully erect posture."

One of the most important and exciting aspects of the Spy discovery was made when the archaeological evidence was critically examined by the experts. It was found that the stone implements taken from the same stratum as the two skeletons belonged to a culture which had already been recognized and named — the Mousterian. It was now over twenty years since Edouard Lartet had investigated the cave at Le Moustier, which had later become the type site for the Mousterian culture. Although many artifacts said to have been made in "Mousterian" times had been brought to light, the positive identity of the makers of these particular palaeolithic tools had remained a mystery. Now it was shown that, since the artifacts from Spy bore so many striking resemblances to those from Le Moustier, it was reasonable to suppose that men of the Neanderthal species had been the makers of the Mousterian culture. Many later discoveries confirmed this theory and in time the Mousterian culture came to be so closely linked with the Neanderthalers that they are sometimes referred to as "Mousterian Men."

This discovery at Spy also played a part in dissipating the theory (already strongly opposed by Thomas Huxley) that the skull from the Neanderthal cave was merely that of an idiot. To most scientists it was now clearly unreasonable to suppose that three similar pathological specimens from the same geological period should have been brought to light in Western Europe within the space of thirty years. It was to be some time, however, before German scientists, including such distinguished men as Dr. Hans Virchow von Holder who looked upon the "Neanderthal Race" as a "creation of fancy," came to accept the general verdict.

It is not surprising to find that scientists of the day were now beginning to think of Neanderthal man as our Pleistocene ancestor. In his physical make up, *Homo neanderthalensis* seemed to represent exactly the sort of "human form with simian characters swarming in the details of his structure" which the early disciples of "Darwinism" had been expecting to find, as they traced the story of man's evolution through an uncomplicated progression of ancestral forms, leading from man back to the apes. It should be remembered, too, that opinion was still prejudiced at this time in favour of the belief that man was of comparatively recent origin, so that in every way it seemed reasonable to accept Neanderthal man as the ideal representative of modern man's ancestral form. In appearance he certainly seemed to fill the role for which he was now cast. His body was short and thickset. The massive head, with its heavy brow ridges and receding chin, was claimed to have had a permanent forward thrust, while the legs, moving, they believed, in a semi-flexed position, gave him a curious shambling gait.

The cultural evidence, too, seemed to support this theory. It suggested that Neanderthal man had developed the mental ability to plan ahead since he had collected flints to shape into consistent patterns for use as weapons against his enemies, and as tools for domestic purposes. At some

54

point, moreover, he had taken man's first step towards civilization and learnt how to make fire. All the evidence which was available at this time seemed to confirm the theory that Neanderthal man represented the ancestral form of present day man in Pleistocene times.

We must now look at a somewhat different story. In 1888 the fossil remains of what came to be known as "Galley Hill Man" were found at a depth of eight feet within the gravels of the hundred foot terrace on the south bank of the River Thames near London. These gravels had been exposed in the Thames valley during commercial operations and they had already been the subject of a geological study. Estimates of the ages of the various strata exposed had been drawn up by several authoritative geologists.

The bones of the Galley Hill human skeleton were first seen in what was later claimed to be an "early Pleistocene" deposit. The finder was a workman who was in the habit of keeping a sharp lookout for fossils on behalf of a Mr. Elliott, a local amateur antiquarian. This workman lost no time in telling his friend about the discovery. Elliott personally removed the skeleton from the matrix and preserved the bones to the best of his ability. He then took them to a highly respected geologist, T. Newton, who immediately offered to describe them. Elliott however, wished to publish his own report on the discovery and therefore retained the remains in his own private "museum." Six years later, having given up all hope of finding time to study the skeleton, he again visited Newton who agreed to make a full and detailed investigation of the Galley Hill remains. Letters (published later by Sir Arthur Keith) were written by

Elliott and another local antiquarian describing the circumstances of the find. These were supported, at a much later date, by a similar report which was sent to Sir Arthur by a schoolmaster, Mr. Keys. These three local antiquarians all testified that they had seen the fossil bones of "Galley Hill Man" *in situ,* projecting from a matrix of clayey loam, and had observed, moreover, that the stratum in which they had been embedded was quite undisturbed.

It was not until 1894 that Newton finally announced the discovery of "Galley Hill Man" in a paper he read to the Geological Society of London, but the discovery belongs to the decade we are considering. Since Newton's reputation for integrity and caution was already established, his announcement that "a man of the Chellean period" who had lived in early Pleistocene times had been discovered in Kent aroused great interest. Unfortunately, as six years had already elapsed since the skeleton had been seen *in situ,* the vital question as to whether "Galley Hill Man" had or had not been intrusively buried into the deposit in which the remains were found could only be answered by taking the word of a group of amateur antiquarians. Discussion of the many problems raised by this discovery was revived some years later when Keith published the results of his own investigation of the Galley Hill remains.

Another important but fully authenticated discovery was made in 1888, and once again it was France that contributed a new and valuable piece of evidence which was to shed further light on the kind of people who had inhabited Europe in Palaeolithic times. It had by now been established that during the several phases of the last Glacial

Epoch at least two types of men had flourished in Europe: the short, stocky, and so-called "primitive" Neanderthalers responsible for the Mousterian culture, and the tall Cromagnons who were associated with the Aurignacian culture. In the autumn of 1888 the remains of a representative of what was regarded as a third race were found in a rock shelter at Raymondon in the commune of Chancelade in Southern France. The explorers had already passed through three occupation levels separated by strata of gravel and silts, containing Magdalenian artifacts, when they reached the bed rock on which the skeleton had been laid. The body, liberally coated and surrounded with red ochre, had clearly been given some form of ritual burial, for it lay upon the rocky floor of the shelter in such a way as to suggest that it had been artifically bound after death, with the arms beneath the head and the knees drawn up until they touched the jaw. Some scientists thought that this burial position was merely designed so that the corpse could be fitted into the smallest possible space, others believed that it was an attempt to simulate the pre-natal position. It was already well known that such a custom was practised by both ancient and modern people, including some Eskimos who bend the bodies of their dead into a sitting posture and then wrap it in a skin.

No controversy arose regarding the geological age of the Chancelade skeleton. Qualified experts had been present when the remains were taken from the matrix, while artifacts of the Magdelenian type, as well as the remains of a rich Pleistocene fauna, had been found in the same stratum. There seems to have been no doubt at any time that the

Chancelade skeleton represented the makers of the Magdalenian phase of the Upper Palaeolithic which flourished
during the closing stages of the Pleistocene.

The remains, which represented a massive and thickset
individual, were taken to the museum at Perigueax, where
they were reconstructed and exhaustively studied by Dr. L.
Testut. His anatomical studies suggested to him that the
muscles of the lower jaw, which are used for mastication,
and those attached to the upper arm bone or humerus,
which play an important part in the act of climbing, had
been especially well developed. The skull itself, which was
long, narrow, and exceedingly high, was reported to have
a brain capacity of 1710 cc., which exceeds that of average
modern Europeans. The face was remarkable for its great
breadth and the very narrow nasal opening. Testut recognized that it had many resemblances to the known skulls
of Cromagnon man, but he nevertheless maintained that
the discovery should be regarded as the type specimen of a
new race of mankind which he named the Chancelade
Race.

This decision was hotly contested by many anthropologists who did not think the differences were great enough
to justify it. Testut's supporters, however, believed that
they now possessed proof of the existence of two distinct
races of man during the Upper Palaeolithic period in Europe: one represented by the "giant" old man of Cromagnon and the other by the comparatively short and stocky
Chancelade man.

It should be noted here that sixteen years earlier, in
1872, three French scientists had observed certain striking

resemblances between the cultures of the Magdalenian reindeer hunters and those of some modern Eskimo peoples.
They had consequently postulated the theory that the European cave dwellers of Upper Palaeolithic times were ancestral to the Eskimos. This view was based on archaeological and ethnographical evidence, strengthened by the
fact that in the snowbound wastes of Greenland and Lab-
rador the Eskimos of modern times are living in an environment similar to that which existed at the time of the
early Magdalenians. Comparisons of the two cultures had
revealed a surprising similarity in many of the artifacts
which distinguished them both, such as bone arrowheads,
spear throwers, ivory pendants and stone tools. There was
also a remarkable resemblance between the beautiful drawings and engravings of both peoples.

From his anatomical studies, Testut now strongly supported this theory. His comparative analysis of the skull of
Chancelade man and that of the modern Eskimo revealed
that both were strongly dolichocephalic (long and narrow
headed), that both had high skulls, and that both had
prominent sagittal ridges. There were also similarities in
the faces, which contained great height and width across
the cheek bones, while the orbits in each case were almost
round in shape. In stature both races were small and had
disproportionately large heads.

A few years later, Professor W. J. Sollas of Oxford, to
whom the subject was of great interest, strongly supported
Dr. Testut's views in a chapter of his famous book *Ancient
Hunters*. He even went so far as to maintain that "the
osteological characters of the Eskimos, which are of a very

special kind, are repeated by the Chancelade skeleton so completely as to leave no reasonable doubt that it represents the remains of a veritable Eskimo who lived in Southern France during the Magdalenian Age."

The theory was therefore now put forward that the Magdalenian hunters had followed in the wake of the great herds of reindeer and other subarctic fauna as they retreated northwards and eastwards during the closing phases of the last European glaciation. It was suggested that both men and animals had then crossed the land bridge which spanned the Bering Straits and eventually spread southwards into the American Continent. Once there, the little reindeer hunters would have found physical conditions similar to those they had left in Europe.

Whether Chancelade man was ancestral to the Eskimos or represented no more than a variant of Cromagnon man (as so many scientists maintained), it was generally acknowledged that science was, at last, in possession of the remains of a man who had lived when the Magdalenian culture had flourished in Europe. The earlier origin of Neanderthal man, Cromagnon man, and Chancelade man was still a mystery; but it was becoming clear that since some form of man had been in existence all through what was then known of the Palaeolithic period, his beginning must be sought in the more remote past. A hitherto unbelievable antiquity for man became an exciting and even an awe-inspiring possibility which was supported by ever-increasing data. In 1889, Boule of Paris went so far as to suggest that since certain genera of animals such as true cats, hyenas, deer and rhinoceros were known to have existed from the Upper Miocene onwards, he saw no reason at all why the genus *Homo* should not have been their contemporary. "I am perfectly convinced," he wrote, "that palaeontologists will someday find the bone remains of our Tertiary ancestors."

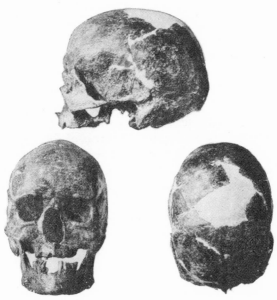

The Chancelade skull, full face and profile. This skull probably one of the several Magdalenian tribal types; it is likely that Eskimos are descended from this stock, with some other admixtures.

CHAPTER VI

1890—1899

Towards the close of the nineteenth century a young Dutch anatomist, Dr. Eugene Dubois, resigned from his post as lecturer in the University of Amsterdam. Stirred and inspired by Darwin's *Descent of Man* and by the results of his own research work, Dubois dreamed of discovering the remains of some fossil creature ancestral to man and yet embodying proof in its morphology of a very primitive status. Darwin had suggested that the remains of early man might very well be found in those areas of the world where the great apes were still living, and had prophesied that Africa would prove to be the birthplace of man. There was nevertheless strong support for the alternative theory that early man's origins might be discovered in Asia where the orang-outans lived. Dubois decided to begin his search in Java.

In those days it was not easy to find money for such a project. The Dutch Government refused to support it and, in the end, Dubois accepted a commission as a surgeon in the Dutch Army and was sent overseas to the Dutch Indies. A less dedicated man might well have been daunted by the task of trying to combine research work with the exhausting duties of an army doctor in the steaming heat of the Indies. It is reported that his fellow officers felt Dubois was supported in all he did by an almost fatalistic confidence in the ultimate success of his search. While they rested, he explored his surroundings in a tireless effort to uncover the prehistoric past.

His sensational discovery was made near the little village of Trinil on the Island of Java. For some time past, Dubois had been excavating a site on the banks of the River Solo near Trinil, and this had yielded him a rich fossil fauna from a stratum of volcanic origin. From the many resemblances between the bones he was finding and those recovered in the Upper Pliocene deposits of the Siwalik Hills of India, more than 2,000 miles away, it seemed to him possible that Java had once formed part of the Asiatic mainland.

The fossil fauna at Trinil, most of which belonged to species that are now extinct, included a hippopotamus with archaic characters, rhinoceros, porcupine, pangolin, horned and antlered ruminants, carnivores (particularly of the cat family), elephants (including a species of the primitive genus *Stegodon*), hyena, otter and a macaque monkey. Finally, after months of hard work, Dubois found the scattered remains of a hominid. The first specimen to be found was a tooth discovered in 1890. This find was shortly followed by that of a skull cap and, in the following year 1891, by that of a femur and then a second tooth. These remains were only separated from each other by a few yards and Dubois was convinced, (a view which was later shared by many scientists), that the remains were those of one single individual which had been scattered by the movements of the waters of the river.

The geological age of this fossiliferous stratum was, naturally, a matter of major importance. Many scientists, like Dubois, attributed it to a late phase of the Upper Pliocene; others preferred to assign it to the early Pleistocene period. These differences of opinion were of no great significance, since there was no real dividing line between the two consecutive geological chapters.

In 1894 Dubois published a monograph on his discovery, in which he claimed that the Trinil fossil was "the precursor of Man," and represented the "intermediate form between the Anthropoids and man." He described his discovery as having a "much larger skull absolutely and relatively to the body mass than in the large apes, but less bulky than in Man: cerebral capacity about two thirds that of Man. Inclination of the nuchal plane of the occiput was much greater than in the large apes. Dentition different from that of the latter, although of archaic form. Femur of human dimensions and suited for walking in the upright position." Dubois, in fact, came to the conclusion that the Trinil remains represented a transitional form between Ape and Man; he therefore named his discovery *Pithecanthropus erectus* (pithecos anthropus) or the "Ape-Man with the upright posture."

From his study of the remains Dubois estimated that *Pithecanthropus erectus* must have weighed about 154 pounds and stood about 5 ft. 8 inches high. The femur was described as being remarkably straight and there seemed to be general agreement among anatomists of that period that *Pithecanthropus* must have walked in an upright position as man does today. It was agreed that had the femur been found alone, there would have been no hesitation in attributing it to *Homo.*

Some of the characters of the skull cap, however, were regarded as being more simian than human, and in Dubois' opinion, "could be compared to that of a gibbon enlarged to twice its size." On the other hand, a study of the brain cast revealed that the parts supposed to be linked with speech, although small, were definitely present. Dubois concluded that *Pithecanthropus* might well have had a rudimentary, but nevertheless articulate, speech.

In orangs, chimpanzees, and gorillas, the brain capacity is generally accepted as varying between 290 cc. and 750 cc. In living human races, the capacity may be as low as 930 cc. and as high as 2000 cc. The brain capacity of *Pithecanthropus* was estimated at 850 cc., and was thus intermediate between that of an ape such as a gorilla and a man with a very low brain capacity, such as an Australian aborigine or a Bushman. In *Pithecanthropus* it was claimed that the association centers of the brain did not approach the "human" level, although the sensation centers were well developed.

Scientific opinion at this time appears to have been sharply divided on the interpretation of the dentition. While Dubois maintained that the two teeth he had found belonged to the hominid form, others considered they were those of a fossil orang. Some years later Professor Henry F. Osborn maintained that they were "more human than those of the gibbon but did not resemble those of man closely enough to positively confirm the prehuman theory." Keith also, later concluded that the teeth were "in the main human," while Boule decided that "since the greatest similarities were with those of the orang . . . they were definitely simian."

Various attempts were made at this time to reconstruct the complete skull of Java man, and at the turn of the century Dubois exhibited a life-size reconstruction of *Pithecanthropus,* as he might have appeared in the flesh. Visitors to the Dutch Indies pavilion at the International Exhibition of 1900 saw the model of a heavily built creature of medium height, standing in the erect position of man, peering out from beneath a thick orbital ridge which protruded above the eyes from a shallow, receding forehead and a flattened skull cap.

What then was this strange but awe-inspiring figure from the remote past? Scientists who had accepted the theory of evolution had been prepared to find that the transitional form, intermediate between man and ape, would exhibit a gradual and simultaneous change in all his parts. In *Pithecanthropus,* however, although the capacity of the brain was lower than any recorded for the most primitive human race, the extensive structural changes necessary for the adaptation of the body to an upright posture had already taken place. *Pithecanthropus* had, apparently, the powers of speech, the upright stance of modern man, and consequently the free use of hands and arms. Was *Pithecanthropus* then to be regarded as a true man, an ape, or, as Dubois maintained, a transitional form intermediate between the two?

All three views were strongly supported and it was even suggested that the Trinil remains were those of a microcephalic idiot. Still others suggested that it was simply a monstrous offspring of a cross between human and simian parents.

The discovery was an international sensation. No other fossil find had led to so many discussions or to so great a conflict of scientific opinion. The controversy raged for many years. "In all its characters," Boule wrote much later in his famous book *Fossil Men,* "this fossil stands in an intermediate position. This is a positive fact admitted by all competent naturalists." There were scientists, however, who considered that *Pithecanthropus* exhibited characters indicating an origin in some form of anthropoid ape and yet with some more evolved features. They postulated the theory that, as the Trinil remains had been found in an area where gibbons were living, they probably represented an extinct giant form of gibbon. In this case, *Pithecanthropus* would have been classed as a highly specialized "cousin," entirely simian.

When Keith studied the evidence some fifteen years later he accepted *Pithecanthropus* as the representative of a very early stage in human evolution, but not the stage reached by mankind at the end of the Pliocene period. It seemed to him highly improbable that the simple brain of *Pithecanthropus* could have evolved into the complex modern form exhibited by the Upper Palaeolithic men of Western Europe during the span of time then allotted to the Pleistocene period, "even if this was estimated at 30,000 years." Furthermore, having studied the complex structural changes which are necessary to adapt the body to an upright posture, he believed it to be unlikely that these

67

could have taken place twice, once in the human ancestry and once in that of *Pithecanthropus*. He suggested, therefore, that all human races must be the descendants of a common stock in which the upright position was already evolved. Moreover, since it seemed improbable that a common ancestor should yield two such divergent races as those of the Negro and the modern European during the brief time span of the Pleistocene, he stressed the necessity of increasing the estimate of man's antiquity.

"The gorilla of today," he wrote in 1915 in his book *The Antiquity of Man,* "is not a human ancestor, but retains, we suppose, in a much higher degree than man does, the stock from which both arose. It is in this light that I would interpret *Pithecanthropus,* a true survival into late Pliocene or early Pleistocene times of an early stage in the true and direct line of human evolution, a stage we may expect to find evolved not in the Pliocene but in the Miocene Period. We may accept *Pithecanthropus* as representing a very early stage in human evolution."

It was becoming evident to anatomists that the vision of man's descent from the apes through an orderly series of primates to *Homo sapiens* was not broad enough, and that the estimate of man's antiquity and the concept of his evolutionary development would have to be greatly expanded in order to account for the diverse types of modern man. The geologists of the period, too, were continually finding it necessary to extend their concept of geological time, and a vast amount of research was being carried out in order to try and establish a definite chronology. The rate of progress of glaciers, alterations in rocks by atmospheric conditions, the hollowing of gorges by natural forces, changes in sea levels and river courses, the composition of lake deposits and many other geological phenomena were being recorded and interpreted. However, time measurements based on these interpretations inevitably varied enormously.

In *Fossil Men,* Boule points out the wide range of figures produced by a number of eminent scientists when estimating the duration of the Pleistocene Epoch. The lowest figure of 10,000 years was proposed by two French geologists, and the highest, of a million years plus, was suggested by the two German geographers, Professors Penck and Bruckner. At the turn of the century, then, scientific opinion was sharply divided concerning the duration of the Pleistocene, and the number and length of the glacial and inter-glacial phases which occurred within its span. It was generally accepted, however, on geological evidence, that during the height of these periods of intense cold, great ice sheets had covered almost a third of the surface of the world, and that the weight of these enormous areas of ice, resting for countless centuries on the northern lands of Europe, Asia and the American continent had greatly changed the surface of the earth beneath.

We must now return once again to France. In 1894 the skeleton of a youth was brought to light at the mill of Les Hoteaux, near Roussillon in France. The bones were found in association with objects of the Magdalenian culture, and had been covered with red ochre. Although this was not regarded as a discovery of major importance, it nevertheless revived the controversy as to whether Palaeolithic man had been mentally capable of venerating his dead by giving them a form of ritual burial. More conclusive evidence was badly needed to convince those who were still in doubt. It was shortly to be produced from the Côte d'Azur where Prince Albert of Monaco had enlisted a talented team to collaborate with him in a systematic exploration of the Grimaldi caves. The excavations were in charge of M. le Canon de Villeneuve. The geological and palaeontological observations which were to furnish Dr. Verneau with a chronological basis for studying any discoveries that might be made, were the responsibility of Boule.

It was in the Grotte des Enfants, already made famous by Rivière's earlier discoveries, that the most spectacular results were obtained. When the excavations in this cave were completed, the scientists found that a vast and exciting page of geological and anthropological history had been uncovered. From the anthropological point of view the work was extremely rewarding. Four human skeletons were brought to light at three different occupation levels, and since the investigations were carried out by experts, the geological age of the remains was not questioned. From a study of the stratigraphy in which the remains of typical glacial and inter-glacial faunas were discovered, Boule came to the conclusion that all the deposits were of Pleistocene age. He also established the fact that the reindeer, contrary to previous opinion, had formed part of the cold climate fauna of Europe as far south as the Côte d'Azur, for its remains were found in association with all the other cold climate animals in the Grotte des Enfants.

These new discoveries did much to dispel some of the

lingering doubts as to whether Palaeolithic man had, in fact, given his dead any form of ritual burial. The geological age of the human remains was established and there seems to have been little doubt in anybody's mind that all four bodies had been deliberately interred. Each was stained with red ochre and surrounded by ornaments. The two skeletons from the upper layers were fully extended, while the two in the lowest layer had been placed in the same contracted position in which earlier Palaeolithic skeletons had been found.

The remains of the two individuals which were found in the upper layers of the cave, in association with objects of the Aurignacian culture, were regarded as definitely representing the Cromagnon type of man. Those found at a depth of eight and a half meters near the rocky floor of the cave exhibited a number of characters said to be shared by "certain modern African races of *Homo sapiens*." Verneau therefore claimed them to be the representatives of a hitherto unknown human variant which he named the Grimaldi race.

The discovery of the so-called "Grimaldi Negroids" was widely discussed and many theories were put forward to explain their presence in a European cave in Palaeolithic times. Verneau did not rule out the possibility that the "Grimaldi Negroids" had some close relationship with the Cromagnons, nor did he deny that they were perhaps the "ancestors of the hunters of the Reindeer Age." After exhaustive research into the subject, however, he maintained that their influence could still be discerned in skeletons of the Neolithic period and that as a race the "Grimaldi Negroids" must have played an important part in Western Europe in the Pleistocene. There was very little support for this view and it was generally agreed that although some negroids had possibly crossed the land bridge which had supposedly joined Africa to Europe in Pleistocene times, they had not become firmly established.

Some three hundred miles to the west, at the foot of the Pyrenees, another systematic exploration was in progress at Mas d'Azil, a small French hamlet which was to achieve international fame as the type station of the Azilian culture. In the Grotte des Enfants, the record of Stone Age man's industries ended with the Aurignacian culture of Cromagnon man. At Mas d'Azil, it began with the succeeding Magdalenian industries and traced the cultural development of man, from the end of the Upper Palaeolithic times to the Neolithic and thence onwards to the Bronze, Copper and Iron Ages.

In 1887 the attention of a French magistrate, Edouard A. Piette, had been drawn to a series of hearths and stone implements which had been exposed to view by workmen in a lofty tunnel, through which the road from St. Girons to Carcassone winds along the course of the River Arize. Piette immediately began his own systematic scientific investigations. They eventually yielded a rich harvest of prehistoric treasure, and contributed another valuable chapter to the story of our ancestors since Palaeolithic times.

Eight years later Piette published the result of his work. He distinguished two layers of Magdalenian culture, the lowest of which rested on bed rock about twenty-four feet above the present level of the River Arize. This yielded a typical Pleistocene fauna which included the remains of many reindeer and implements that had been made from their bones and antlers. Separated from this layer by a deposit of thick, yellow loam, indicative of a long and continuous period of water deposition, another human occupation level was uncovered in which Piette brought to light many implements of a later stage of the Magdalenian culture, including harpoon heads together with engraved and sculpted bone figurines. Above these two Magdalenian layers, and separated from them by another thick deposit of loam, Piette discovered a human occupation level in which he found the evidence of a hitherto unrecognized Stone Age culture. In his opinion it represented a transitional stage of development between the Palaeolithic and true Neolithic Ages. He named it the Azilian. The geological and faunal evidence showed that a moist climate had succeeded the closing phases of the final or Würm glaciation. It seemed that vast forests had sprung up on the previously bleak steppe lands which had characterized southern Europe during the Great Ice Age.

The Reindeer Age was over. The great herds of those animals that had provided Palaeolithic hunters with food and skins and material for his tools and weapons had followed the retreating ice sheets northwards. The place of the reindeer in Europe was now taken by the forest dwelling stag. Harpoons and other implements in the Azilian layer were made from the bones and antlers of this type of deer. Moreover, there was no longer any trace of that superb artistry which had characterized so much of the Magdalenian culture. Some of the stone implements, however, showed traces of polishing, while a number of pebbles were brought to light on which a variety of geometric designs had been painted with peroxide of iron. This strange discovery aroused widespread interest, and many theories were put forward to try and explain the riddle of these decorated stones. Were they symbolic signs used in religious rites? Did they perhaps form part of the equipment for a primitive monetary system? Were they evidence of a Palaeolithic school? In his book *Ancient Hunters,* Professor Sollas records that a Tasmanian woman who had been seen arranging a similar collection of painted pebbles on the ground told a questioner that each stone represented an absent friend. Her stones were, moreover, reported to resemble those found by Piette but in view of the time gap, there could clearly be no cultural link between the two occurances. The meaning of the painted pebbles of Mas d'Azil remained an unsolved problem.

The remains of two human skeletons were found in the Azilian layer, but they were in such a poor state of preservation that the anatomists were unable to discover much about the type of man who had been responsible for the Azilian culture. Immediately above the Azilian layer, Piette uncovered evidence of a culture which clearly belonged to the New Stone Age or Neolithic, thus supporting his theory that the Azilian layer was a transitional stage between the true Upper Palaeolithic and the early phases of the Neolithic.

In 1891, while Dubois was recovering the remains of *Pithecanthropus* in Java, a human skull had been found at Brünn, some sixty miles from Vienna, during commercial excavations. The remains of a cold climate fauna which included woolly mammoth, woolly rhinoceros, giant deer and reindeer were excavated from the same deposit. The skull, which became known as Brünn I, was regarded by some scientists of the time as representing a transitional form between Neanderthal man and *Homo sapiens,* and was referred to as a member of the "Brünn Race."

Not far away excavations were in progress at Předmost, in Moravia, where a remarkable site had been discovered containing the remains of nearly a thousand mammoths. These bones were associated with tools of stone and bone and ivory, all typical of the Aurignacian culture. In 1894 Professor Maschka, who was in charge of these excavations, uncovered a huge Palaeolithic burial ground from which nearly fifty human skeletons were obtained. Much discussion took place as to whether these "Mammoth Hunters of Předmost" were representatives of the "The Brünn Race," but in time they came to be regarded as no more than minor variants of the Cromagnon race. The few visible differences were attributed either to environment or to racial intermixture.

In 1899 numerous remains of Neanderthal Man were discovered by Professor Gorjanovič-Kramberger at Krapina in what was then known as Croatia and is now part of Yugoslavia. The rock shelter which he was investigating had been close to the banks of the River Krapinica in Pleistocene times, but is now many feet above water level. In the course of his work, he uncovered thousands of animal bones, hundreds of human bones and teeth, and many stone tools. The latter were assigned in general terms to the Mousterian culture. Opinions regarding the geological age of this rich site were divided; although the animal remains represented a typical Mid-Pleistocene fauna, they also included specimens of an ancient form of rhinoceros (*Rhinoceros mercki*) that was more usually regarded as belonging with the "Lower Pleistocene" of that time. According to some scientists, however, this did not necessarily indicate a Lower Pleistocene age, since this animal was known to have persisted much longer than any other typical lower Pleistocene species, such as the hippopotamus and the extinct elephant (*Elephas antiquus*).

Keith, when discussing this discovery in 1915, stressed its importance to the anatomist on the grounds that the Krapina human remains exhibited typical Neanderthaloid characters, and represented at least ten individuals of both sexes and several ages. Thus, for the first time, scientists had an opportunity to study the children and adolescents of Neanderthal Man.

The skulls of man and ape were already known to bear close superficial resemblances to each other during infancy and childhood, after which, although human skulls change very little during growth, those of apes gradually acquire the distinguishing specialized features of this group. From a study of the remains from the Krapina burial site, it appeared that the skulls of the infants of this race were more like those of modern man than were the skulls of the adult individuals. The great brow ridges of Neanderthal Man apparently only formed when he reached maturity.

Nine different human occupation levels were eventually uncovered in this shelter, and since many of the human bones had been broken open and charred by fire, it was suggested that these men of Krapina had practised cannibalism.

The 19th Century was drawing to its close. It had witnessed the shattering of many of man's beliefs regarding his own origin. Darwin's theory of evolution was beginning to capture the imagination of the world, and there was a growing tendency for the Church to try and reconcile its own teachings with the new concept of human evolution.

CHAPTER VII
1900—1909

By the beginning of the twentieth century, Prehistory was becoming an academic study and the search into the prehistoric past for the remains of early man was no longer regarded as an occupation for naturalists, amateurs, and cranks. The dawning concept of the immense duration of the world and the growing conviction that all the evidence was slowly but surely beginning to indicate a hitherto unbelievable antiquity for man himself, was also attracting the attention of the popular press and stirring the imagination of many thinkers.

In scientific circles, authorities were stressing the value of discoveries which were the results of long term planning and systematic investigations, such as those made at Mas d'Azil and on the Côte d'Azur; they urged their colleagues to use similar scientific methods when undertaking future explorations. Other long-term investigations initiated in the previous century resulted in a number of remarkable discoveries in the first decade of the twentieth century. These discoveries constituted a major contribution to the story of the Neanderthalers, and also presented science with the fossil jaw of an individual whose status in the human family was to remain a matter for argument for many years to come.

The controversial jaw was found near Heidelberg, Germany in 1907 in a sand pit beside the River Elsenz, in the village of Mauer. For many years the Mauer Sands had attracted the attention of geologists and palaeontologists because of the rich fossil fauna which had been found, from time to time, by the men who worked in the pits. These finds had included *Elephas antiquus*, the Etruscan rhinoceros, wild boar, roe deer, red deer, elk, bison, wild cat and, among many others, the remains of a particular type of horse which was regarded as being a transitional form between the extinct horse *Equus stenoris* and the modern horse. These animals indicated the warm or temperate climate of an inter-glacial period, when Europe must have been covered by forests and meadow lands. The various species were recognized as being the same as, or closely related to, those which had been found in what were then regarded as Lower Pleistocene deposits in France.

In 1907, the owner of this sand pit sent for Dr. Otto Schoetensack of Heidelberg University, who had been visiting the Mauer sand pit almost daily for many years. On his arrival he was shown a fossil human jaw which the workmen had found on the previous day following a fall of sand from the lower level of the pit face. Dr. Schotensack assigned the stratum from which the jaw *seemed* to have been derived to an early stage of the Pleistocene period, and recognized twenty-four strata above it. He named this discovery *Homo heidelbergensis* and, in 1908, published a memoir in which it was claimed that the Mauer jawbone exhibited "a combination of features never before found in any fossil or recent man."

The jawbone was accepted as being unquestionably human, but its mixture of modern and primitive characters suggested to some authorities that, like the brain case of *Pithecanthropus,* it represented just what might be expected of "an intermediate form between man and ape." No other part of the skeleton was ever found and it was commonly supposed that, when the jawbone became separated from the skull, it had drifted downstream.

The skull was in a good state of preservation and the teeth were all reported to have been intact on first discovery. As preserved today however, some of the teeth on the left side of the jaw are missing. (The early reports say these were knocked off by the workman with the point of his shovel.) A study of the inner surface of the mandible at the point where the tongue muscles would be attached led Dr. Schotensack to believe that *Homo heidelbergensis* had probably possessed the beginnings of articulate speech. After studying the dentition, some authorities were inclined to believe that *Homo heidelbergensis* might prove to be no more than a primitive variety of Neanderthal man, or, as Professor Osborn later suggested, "a Neanderthaler in the making, that is, a more primitive, more powerful and more ape-like ancestral form."

Anthropological opinion was sharply divided as to the exact status which should be accorded to this ancient representative of man and, although it was described as *Homo heidelbergensis,* there was a large body of opinion that maintained that it should be accorded distinct generic rank and referred to as *Palaeoanthropus heidelbergensis.* This discovery was acknowledged at the time to be among the most important and exciting then recorded by prehistorians. It established the fact that, as long ago as the earliest stages of the Pleistocene period (as then defined), man had been living in Europe.

Another find which was to prove of outstanding importance was made in 1908 by three French priests whose work in prehistory was already well-known in scientific circles. The priests, MM. the Abbés A. Bouyssonie, J. Bouyssonie and Bardon, had undertaken the excavation of a small cave near the village of La Chapelle-aux-Saints in the Department of the Corrèze, in southern France. Below the modern floor of the cave, they found the remains of a cold climate fauna which included the woolly rhinoceros, extinct bison and reindeer. Here, in a shallow rectangular depression, they came across the skeleton of a Neanderthal-type man. It lay extended full length on its back, with the head pointing to the east. Beside it were Mousterian type artifacts as well as fragments of red ochre. Across the skull lay several limb bones of bison, one of which was still connected with some of the smaller bones of the foot and toes — thus suggesting that the flesh had been on the bones when they had been placed with the human body. Although it was clear that the cave had been occupied for long centuries after the body had been laid to rest, the stratum above the burial bore no trace of having been disturbed. The priests stated their conviction that they had opened up the grave of a Neanderthaler who had been given a formal burial by his contemporaries.

The very possibility of any burial rites having taken place in Upper Palaeolithic times, had at one time seemed inconceivable both to science and the Church. Now the three priests reported they had found the grave of a strange primitive creature of the Lower Palaeolithic age, who had not only been carefully buried, but even equipped with the necessities for a spiritual journey. Incredible though it seemed at the time, scientists began to wonder whether Neanderthal man might not have already developed a belief in a life after death.

The remains from the cave at La Chapelle-aux-Saints were in an excellent state of preservation. They included the skull and most of the bones of the body. Boule of Paris carried out what was widely acclaimed as "the most thorough and exact investigation ever made of an ancient human skeleton." He maintained that the body was that of an old man of the Neanderthal type, and assigned its geological age to the Pleistocene period. His memoir on this skeleton was published in 1908, and contained the most detailed information about the anatomical structure of Neanderthal man then available to the scientific world.

In 1909, it became known that still another representative of the Neanderthal race had been found during the previous year, at Le Moustier in the Dordogne district of France. This discovery was made by a Swiss collector, Herr Otto Hauser, when he was excavating a site on the banks of the River Vézère, not far from the rock shelter in which Edouard Lartet had previously found evidence of the culture which he had named Mousterian. The skeleton was found five feet below the floor of the shelter and represented that of a sixteen year old Neanderthal youth. Here again there was evidence of some form of ritual burial, for typical Mousterian artifacts had been laid beside the body. This find had been uncovered somewhat secretively, in the presence of some scientists from Eastern Europe, and its importance was held by many French prehistorians to be sadly diminished by the poverty of the geological and palae-ontological evidence supporting it. Furthermore, the resto-ration of the skull, which was badly crushed, had been undertaken by Professor H. Klaatsch of Germany, who, to use the words of Keith, "had not been altogether fortunate in the reconstruction of the fragments." This discovery, however, had the distinction of being the first representa-tive of the Neanderthal race to be found at the type locality of the Mousterian culture.

In 1909, further human bones were uncovered in a rock shelter at La Ferrassie, where systematic investigations had been in progress for some ten years. They, too, were found associated with a number of Mousterian type implements, and were taken from the matrix in the presence of several scientists, including Boule himself. The remains were described as those of a male member of the Neander-thal race, and the stratum in which they were discovered was claimed to be of comparable age to that in which the skeleton of "the Old Man" had been found at La Chapelle-aux-Saints. Above this stratum at La Ferrassie was another occupation level containing implements of the more ad-vanced Aurignacian culture, which showed no trace of having been disturbed by the interment of a body. Con-tinued excavations at this site brought to light the remains of a female of the same Neanderthal type, and later still, those of three children. There was, however, no evidence to suggest that these bodies had been given any form of burial, and it was therefore conjectured that they were the members of a single family who had been killed by a rock fall.

Cleaning and reconstruction of the skull of this male Neanderthaler, which was almost as complete as that from' La Chapelle-aux-Saints, was again carried out in Boule's laboratory in Paris.

Another important and exciting discovery was made in 1909 by Herr Otto Hauser, during his excavations of a terrace on the side of the valley of the River Couze at Combe-Capelle. He had uncovered a layer containing implements of the Solutrean industry near the present day surface and, below this, separated by sterile strata, he found three layers containing evidence of Upper, Middle and finally Lower Aurignacian cultures. In the lowest level, he came upon a human skeleton. The knees were bent, the thighs drawn up and a number of flint implements and shells (which had been perforated for ornamentation) had been laid beside the body. Among these products of an early phase of the Aurignacian culture which had been interred with the body, the investigators found a single-pointed but well-made hand axe. Boule records that an attempt was made by Hauser to establish this skeleton as "the type specimen of a particular species under the name *Homo aurignacensis hauseri*," but it was more generally accepted to be a representative of the Cromagnon race.

Thus, in the Dordogne country, the skeletons of two completely different types of man were discovered in successive geological layers, at sites which were only a few miles apart. It was now becoming clear that southern France had been occupied in Pleistocene times both by the primitive Neanderthalers, and, either at the same time or immediately afterwards, by the Cromagnons. The latter were a race of men who were as highly evolved in the structure of their bones and brains as the men of today. It began to seem probable, therefore, that if Neanderthal man really represented an ancestor of a modern type of man, that stage of evolution must have taken place long before Mousterian times.

Archaeologists who had by now been given the opportunity of studying a very large number of Mousterian artifacts, also supported this theory. The implements made by Neanderthal man, though considered crude compared with those of later cultures such as the Aurignacian, Solutrean and Magdalenian, were nevertheless regarded as the products of a very highly skilled technique which must have been perfected over a long period of time by successive generations of Neanderthalers.

In the enthusiastic search for new knowledge, another valuable discovery of Neanderthal hominids was made to the northwest of La Chapelle-aux-Saints, in a rock shelter which was being carefully excavated at La Quina. Here Dr. Henri-Martin, a local doctor, uncovered three strata belonging to different phases of the Mousterian culture. Each yielded a medley of stone objects such as awls, scrapers, saws, lance-heads and other Mousterian implements, which the ancient hunters had shaped and left behind them. The remains of charred and broken animal bones found here, as on so many other Mousterian living floors in Europe, suggested that Neanderthal man had lived mainly by hunting. Wild horse seemed to have been a most popular diet, but there was plenty of evidence to show that many other animals, including the cave bear and the great woolly mammoth, had been successfully killed. Archaeologists deduced from the broken bones that the Neanderthalers were fond of extracting the marrow before discarding the bones, and inferred from the marks of fire that these people probably roasted their meat.

A little later, Dr. Henri-Martin found a human astragalus, (an ankle bone), in the lowest part of the early Mousterian level of this rock shelter. It was found in direct association with the remains of fossilized animals such as reindeer and a primitive form of ox. Owing to its distinctive morphology, this ankle bone was regarded as part of an individual of the Neanderthal type, and in the following year, the greater part of a skull and the skeleton of another, but smaller, probably female individual was brought to light.

During the excavations which took place at La Quina, a number of spherical limestone balls were uncovered, suggesting that Mousterian man had mastered the use of the "bolas." Many of these balls had apparently been shaped by hand, and are thought to have provided the weight which the Neanderthal hunters had made for this useful hunting weapon. The bolas, still in use by some South American tribes, is made by selecting several stones of unequal size, usually between two and five in number, and attaching each to a long, leather thong. When the thongs have been tied together at the loose ends, the weapon is ready to be taken on the hunt. It is aimed at the legs of a running animal and, if the throw is a good one, the weighted thongs twist round the legs of the prey and bring it to the ground.

These new discoveries of well-preserved *Homo neanderthalensis* revived an interest in the skull found in Gibraltar in 1848 which had been placed in the Museum of the Royal College of Surgeons in London. Geological and archaeological data about the site at Forbes Quarry, where this skull had originally been found, were now badly needed by the anatomists who were studying the skull. Towards the close of the decade now under review, Professor Duckworth of Cambridge went out to Gibraltar to explore the north face of the Rock. His search was unrewarding, but an examination of other caves in the same area yielded a quantity of stone implements worked in the typical Mousterian manner. Comparison of the matrix in which these implements were embedded with that which still filled the nose cavity and orbits of the Gibraltar skull in London showed that both were composed of an identical mixture of sand and limestone.

Thus, sixty-two years after its discovery, the importance of this skull was finally established. Although it came to be unequivocally accepted as the remains of an individual of the Neanderthal type, it was regarded by some scientists as a variant of the race. Certain affinities were observed between the remains of the Neanderthalers found at Krapina and the skull discovered at Gibraltar, and both appeared to differ from the more classical but contemporary remains which had been found in southern France and Belgium. These observations supported the rapidly growing conviction that the early world of man had been a complex one and that Neanderthal man, like modern man, had been divided into a number of different races.

Well-authenticated data about Neanderthal man were now rapidly accumulating, and as a result of the discoveries made at La Chapelle-aux-Saints, Le Moustier, La Ferrassie and La Quina, scientists were beginning to revise their views regarding his place in the story of evolution. Anatomists who had given much thought to the Neanderthal remains came to the conclusion that while many of the structural peculiarities were somewhat simian, certain adaptations and specializations were definitely peculiar to *Homo neanderthalensis*. They no longer believed, therefore, that they were dealing with modern man's Pleistocene ancestor, but rather with a form of man that was totally different from any modern race. The differences which separated Neanderthal man from any modern man were held to be greater than those which separated the most divergent of modern human races from each other.

The story of the Neanderthalers was now taking shape. It appeared that during countless centuries of the "Lower Pleistocene" they had successfully dominated the bleak European scene, battling with bears, hyenas and lions for possession of the caves and shelters they needed for protection against the bitter climate.

About this time as we have seen, the Cromagnon and Chancelade races were arriving in western Europe and the available evidence indicates that both were superior in physique and intelligence to the Neanderthalers. Scientists therefore began to ask themselves whether the latter had been killed off by the newcomers as they competed with

88

them for the caves and rock shelters or whether the Neanderthalers had been forced out onto the open tundras where they must have succumbed to the winter weather. The general view in any case was that the Neanderthal race when it found itself in competition with a more advanced people, rapidly gave way and eventually died out completely. The earlier idea that Neanderthal man might have evolved into *Homo sapiens* was widely abandoned and he began to be regarded as no more than an extinct side branch of the human family.

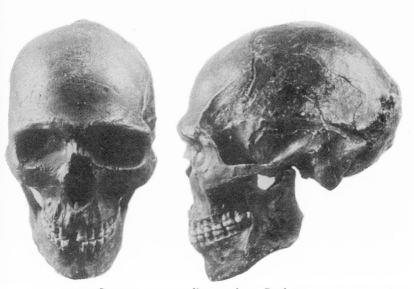

Cromagnon man discovered at Predmost.

CHAPTER VIII
1910—1919

It must be stressed here, once again, that while authenticated discoveries of fossil man were enabling scientists to trace man's ancestry back beyond the frontiers of recorded history, other scientific data about the world of the past and its flora and fauna were rapidly accumulating. It is interesting to note with what enthusiasm amateur antiquarians were now contributing to this ever expanding knowledge of Natural History in its widest sense.

In England many of them had been inspired by the work of the Reverend Gilbert White, whose book, *The Natural History and Antiquities of Selborne,* 1789, is still read even today. His "disciples" spent much of their leisure searching for and recording the antiquities, the fauna and flora, as well as the geology and folklore of their home counties. It was such a man, Charles Dawson, a lawyer, amateur geologist and antiquarian, who was instrumental in sparking off one of the longest and most violent scientific controversies (*) ever associated with the study of prehistory.

(*) In this chapter we shall consider the circumstances surrounding the discovery and the description of the Piltdown skull and mandible. In Chapter XII, we shall discuss the exposure of this fraud, the perpetration of which did so much to cloud the minds of writers on human evolution for many years to come.

90

Dawson is reported as having been a "big man of ample girth." He was a successful lawyer and, apparently, a genial companion. His insatiable curiosity drove him to investigate a wide range of subjects of both prehistoric and historic interest. "Nothing," one of his friends wrote of him later, "came amiss to his alert observation." From boyhood onwards however, it was archaeology and geology which claimed most of his leisure time, and when he was still a young man his collection of local fossils was so impressive that it was accepted by the British Museum of Natural History in London. At an early age too, he was elected a Fellow of the Geological Society of London, thus coming into contact with men of science and gaining the respect of such distinguished people as Sir Arthur Keith and Sir Arthur Smith Woodward (at that time Dr. Smith Woodward), Keeper of Geology at the British Museum of Natural History. In his own local circle, Dawson was sometimes referred to as "The Sussex Wizard."

In 1912 Dawson announced the discovery of the Piltdown fossils which became an overnight sensation and made his name world-famous. The first intimation that a discovery of fossil human skull fragments had been made near Piltdown Common, Sussex, appeared in *Nature* on December 5th, 1912. "Remains of human skull and mandible," it reported, "considered to belong to the early Pleistocene period, have been discovered by Mr. Charles Dawson in a gravel-pit in the basin of the River Ouse, north of Lewes, Sussex. Much interest has been aroused in the specimen owing to the exactitude with which its geological age is said to have been fixed, and it will form the subject of a paper by Charles Dawson and Dr. Smith Woodward to be read before the Geological Society on December 18th." Since *Nature* went to press on the 18th, it was impossible for a report of this meeting to be included in the issue in which the preliminary report appeared on the 19th December, but more detailed references were made to the Piltdown fossils in an article in this issue. These, once more, stressed the importance and the great antiquity of the discoveries. Even before these preliminary notes appeared, rumours of a find in Sussex which might turn out to be of a sensational nature, had begun to leak out. The popular press was quick to seize upon and elaborate its dramatic possibilities. Asia had already presented science with the Java skull cap, Germany with the primitive Heidelberg jaw; was it now to be England's turn to startle the world by the discovery of some strange prehistoric creature who might very well turn out to be "The Missing Link"? Imagination ran riot.

On December 18th, 1912, Dawson and Smith Woodward gave their account of these remarkable finds before the meeting of the Geological Society in London. Many distinguished scientists from all over England, as well as a few from the Continent, were packed into an overcrowded hall. The atmosphere was tense with excitement as Dawson opened the proceedings. He began his account with the following remarks:

"Several years ago, I was walking along a farm road close to Piltdown Common, Fletching (Sussex), when I noticed that the road had been mended with some peculiar brown flints not usual in the district. On inquiry I was astonished to learn that they were dug from a gravel-bed on the farm and shortly afterwards I visited the place, where two labourers were at work digging the gravel for small repairs to the roads. As this excavation was situated about four miles to the north of the limit where the occurence of flints overlying the Wealdon strata is recorded, I was much interested and made a close examination of the bed. I asked the workmen if they had found bones or other fossils there. As they did not appear to have noticed anything of the sort, I urged them to preserve anything that they might find.

"Upon one of my subsequent visits to the pit," Dawson then told his audience, "one of the men handed to me a small portion of an unusually thick human parietal bone. I immediately made a search but could find nothing more, nor had the men noticed anything else . . . and, although I made many subsequent searches, I could not hear of any further find, nor discover anything — in fact the bed seemed to be quite unfossiliferous.

"It was not until some years later, in the autumn of 1911, on a visit to the spot, that I picked up among the rain-washed spoil heaps of the gravel-pit another and larger piece belonging to the frontal region of the same skull, including a portion of the left superciliary ridge."

Dawson then went on to say that he had examined a cast of the Heidelberg jaw and, as it had occured to him that the proportions of this Piltdown skull were "similar to those of that specimen," he had taken it to his friend, Smith Woodward for "comparison and determination." Smith Woodward had been immediately impressed with the importance of the discovery and the two men decided to work together, as they had on previous occasions, and make "a systematic search among the spoil-heaps and gravel" as soon as the pit had dried out after the winter rain. Accordingly, they gave up "as much time as they could spare since last spring (1912), in the hopes of finding more fragments of the human remains."

Dawson then went on to discuss, in some detail, the gravel deposits and the geology of the area in which the fossil remains had been found, and followed this by announcing abruptly that "Apparently the whole or greater portion of this human skull had been shattered by the workmen, who had thrown away the pieces unnoticed. Of these we recovered, from the spoil-heaps, as many fragments as possible. In a somewhat deeper depression of the undisturbed gravel, I found the right half of a human mandible. So far as I could judge, guiding myself by the position of a tree three or four yards away, the spot was identical with that upon which the men were at work when the first portion of the cranium was found several years ago. Smith Woodward also dug up a small portion of the occipital bone of the skull from within a yard of the point where the jaw was discovered, and at precisely the same level." Dawson then gave a description of the associated animal remains, all of which he said, were "highly mineralized with iron oxide."

He also discussed the flint implements or "eoliths" which had been found during the course of their work, and concluded by discussing the "age of the human skull and mandible." "Preferring," he said, "to err on the side of caution," he assigned the Piltdown remains to the beginning of the Pleistocene period.

Smith Woodward then exhibited his reconstruction of the Piltdown skull (which he later modified). It was at once apparent to the audience that the creature it represented must have been a quite extraordinary mixture of man and ape. In describing the skull, Woodward drew attention to the peculiar thickness of the bones of the vault of the skull which were 11-12 mm. thick: approximately double that of the average thickness of comparable modern European skull bones, and nearly double that of the skulls of the Neanderthal race. In his opinion, he asserted, the characters of the skull were essentially human, while the jawbone, which was light in comparison to the skull bones, appeared "to be almost precisely that of an ape, with nothing human except the molar teeth." Smith Woodward then discussed the status which should be accorded to the Piltdown fossils and proposed that they be regarded as "the type of a new genus of the family Hominidae, to be named *Eoanthropus dawsoni* in honour of its discoverer."

In discussing the age of *Eoanthropus dawsoni*, Smith Woodward pointed out that since, in his opinion, it was almost (if not absolutely) of the same geological age as *Homo heidelbergensis*, it would seem that "by the end of the Pliocene epoch the representatives of man in Western Europe were already differentiated into widely divergent groups." He ended by stating that he believed "Mousterian man was a degenerate offshoot of early man and probably became extinct; while surviving man may have arisen directly from the primitive source of which the Piltdown skull provides the first discovered evidence."

In the full published report of this memorable meeting

which appeared in April 1913, there was an Appendix by Dr. Grafton Elliot Smith (later Sir Grafton Elliot Smith), the great expert on the human brain. In this preliminary report on the cranial cast which had been made from Smith Woodward's original reconstruction of the Piltdown skull, Dr. Elliot Smith maintained that "it was the most primitive and most simian brain so far recorded; one, moreover, such as might reasonably have been expected to be associated, in one and the same individual, with the mandible which so definitely indicates the zoological rank of its original possessor."

The names of two men, the genial Charles Dawson and the highly respected Dr. Smith Woodward, were now publicly linked with the discoveries made near Piltdown Common. The name of the third man, Father Pierre Teilhard de Chardin, who according to many people, including Sir Arthur Keith, "shared in all the toils at Piltdown," was not mentioned at all at the Geological Society meeting on December 18th, 1912. In a footnote to the published account of the meeting, however, Dawson wrote that "Father P. Teilhard, S.J. who accompanied us on one occasion, discovered one of the implements . . . "

Father Teilhard de Chardin's name was in fact already known to the Geological Society. Only a month previously, at their November Meeting, Professor Albert Charles Seward of Cambridge had reported on a collection of plants from the Weald obtained by Dawson with the assistance of two Jesuit priests, Father Pelletier and the thirty year old Father Teilhard. During the discussion which followed the meeting it was mentioned that Father Teilhard, who had first become interested in geology in Egypt, had been teaching at the Jesuit College in Hastings for the past four years, during which time he had made Dawson's asquaintance.

From the records, it appears that it was Teilhard who made the next important discovery at Piltdown: he is reported to have picked out a canine tooth from a spread of rain-washed gravel in August, 1913. The probable size and shape of this tooth had already been the subject of many discussions, and scientists had been hoping for just such a discovery. On investigation, the tooth was found to conform so closely to Woodward's original predictions as to size. shape and evidence of wear, that some of the sceptics were converted to his views regarding "Piltdown Man."

Supporters of Darwin's theory of evolution had long believed that evidence would one day be discovered of a human race that had possessed great canines shaped like those of the anthropoid apes. It was no surprise to them, therefore, to learn from Woodward that the canines of Piltdown Man had been "pointed, projecting and shaped as in anthropoid apes."

The excitement engendered by the news of Dawson's discoveries in the heart of Sussex can hardly be exaggerated. They created even more of an international sensation than had either the finding of the Trinil skull cap, or that of the Heidelberg jaw. Repercussions from the scientific world began to be recorded almost immediately and a spate of publications on the subject appeared in many countries. The keynote of all the discussions, then and for many years to come, was the question of whether a skull which was so essentially like that of present day man, could possibly be associated with such an ape-like jaw.

In 1915, fragments of a second so-called representative of the Piltdown type were reported to have been found by Dawson at a site which was never identified, but was said to be some distance away from the scene of the original discoveries. Though its relationship with the Piltdown fossils was never established, the discovery won many converts to Woodward's views.

In 1916 Dawson died, and in spite of a few further desultory excavations, no more field evidence was ever brought to light of the enigmatical "Piltdown Man." By now, the whole world had been caught up in World War I. Father Teilhard was serving as a padre to the French Armed Forces, and the Piltdown fossils were in the care of Woodward at the British Museum of Natural History.

Even at this stage of the Piltdown story, and with only that knowledge then available to science, the many features which should have pointed the finger of doubt at the discovery (and indeed did so to a number of scientists, especially those outside England, mainly in America and France) were clearly to be seen. In the first place the glaring disharmony of the skull and jaw was clear to both the supporters and opponents of Woodward's views. Secondly, it seems odd, now in 1968, that apparently no suspicion of forgery was aroused by the fact that the one piece which would have completely disproved the supposed association of the jaw and skull — the articular knob or condyle of the mandible, was conveniently missing. Thirdly, there was the quite extraordinary vagueness of Dawson's report to the

Geological Society on December 18th, 1912. It was made by a man reputed to be "a keen observer," a successful lawyer and therefore used to estimating the importance of evidence of fact and of detail. Yet, as he announced the most important discovery of his life to an audience of distinguished scientists, he did so without once mentioning a single actual date. Consequently the chronological sequence of events which led up to the finding of the Piltdown fossils, prior to the Geological Meeting of 1912, was never fully established. This contributed to the many confusions and contradictions which appeared in later versions of the story.

It is interesting also to see that Sir Arthur Keith, who made exhaustive studies of the Piltdown material, nearly arrived at the correct solution of the problem of the association of the skull and jawbone. In all his discussions of the skull parts in *Antiquity of Man* in 1915, he was at pains to show that they were in every way like *Homo sapiens*. In his chapters on the jaw and teeth, however, he showed that fundamentally these were like those of an ape. Had he followed his own published precept that "we must put our preconceptions aside," he could scarcely have failed to come to the correct conclusion — that the skull and the jaw could *not* belong to one and the same creature.

Without any further evidence of Piltdown Man to support the many theories postulated in order to try and solve the riddle presented by the jaw and skull, this sensational discovery was inevitably put in a "suspense account." It was not, however, the end of the story. Casts of the Piltdown skull stood on the shelves of laboratories and museums all over the world, and from time to time the old

99

arguments would be revived. In 1948, thirty six years after the announcement of the Piltdown discovery, Keith wrote "The Piltdown Enigma is still far from a final solution." A few years later (see Chapter XII) in a Bulletin of the British Museum of Natural History, of 21st November 1953, "Piltdown Man" was scientifically exposed for what it was — a gigantic and cruel hoax.

Meanwhile at Swanscombe, which lies in the Thames valley not far from Galley Hill, thousands of flint implements regarded as belonging to the Chellean and Acheulean cultures, were now being recovered from gravel deposits which, according to the geologists, were a direct extension of the stratum in which the remains of "Galley Hill Man" had been discovered.

Keith, who at this time was writing a major review of the fossil remains of man, made a special new study of the Galley Hill skull and skeleton. As a result of checking the geological evidence, he supported Mr. Newton's view that "Galley Hill Man" represented one of the makers of the hand axe culture and had lived in England during what he called the "River Drift" times, during the Pleistocene. On the anatomical level, he claimed that the Galley Hill skeleton was that of a man of moderate height, exhibiting no features that could be classed as Neanderthaloid, nor any simian characters other than those which were also to be seen in the skeletons of men of the modern type. "Galley Hill Man," he wrote, "represents no strange species of mankind; he belongs to the same type as modern man."

These views met with a good deal of opposition. Sir John Evans, who was present at a meeting where they came under discussion, expressed his doubts regarding the antiquity of the remains, and suggested that "the occurrence of a nearly perfect specimen in the matrix seemed to imply some form of burial." He was strongly opposed by those scientists who still clung to the belief that any form of burial must have been introduced by recent man, and were not yet prepared to accept the idea that Palaeolithic man could have been capable of any act involving imagination or spiritual awareness.

The theory that *Homo neanderthalensis* represented the ancestral form of man in Mid-Pleistocene times, was now beginning to lose ground. Nevertheless, the argument of his ancestry was used as an additional reason to refute "Galley Hill Man's" claim to any great antiquity. Most scientists of the time regarded it as clearly impossible that a primitive type of man could have lived in continental Europe at the same time as a different type in England. Looking at the world around them, they saw that it was peopled by many races which were all no more than variants of a single species of modern man, and as they unfolded the history of the remote prehistoric past, they expected to find that any ancient population would be made up of a similar collection of variants of a single species.

Echoes of the fierce controversies which raged over the geological age of "Galley Hill Man" were prolonged for many years. Eventually it was generally accepted that the deposit in which the skeleton had been found must have been below the level of the river during Pleistocene times. This being so, it was argued that the skeleton was unlikely to have remained intact through the centuries which had elapsed before the level of the water had dropped. It seemed far more likely that the Galley Hill skeleton was of relatively recent origin, and was an intrusive burial into the gravel deposit in which it was found.

Professor Boule summed up his own view as well as that of many of his colleagues when he maintained that, "since no geologists had been present when the remains were discovered, it was impossible to authenticate Galley Hill Man's antiquity." "We are determined," he declared, "to consign to oblivion all osteological evidence the high antiquity of which is not absolutely assured."

In time, the controversy about the geological age of "Galley Hill Man" died away and the discovery was put into a "suspense account" until finally fluorine dating indicated a far more recent age for "Galley Hill Man" than Keith and his supporters had estimated.

While Europe was still echoing with the story of the "Missing Link" from Piltdown Common, news came from the other side of the world that the first discovery of the remains of fossil man had been made in Australia. This long hoped for report aroused great interest among the anthropologists of the day.

Millions of years ago, during the geological period of the earth's history known as the Cretaceous, Australia had been joined by land to Asia and its flora and fauna were known to have been similar to that which dominated the Asian mainland. By the beginning of the Tertiary period, however, the land bridges had been submerged by the sea and Australia had become a vast island which was to remain isolated from all contact with the outside world for countless centuries.

Rumours of the existence of this great land mass reached the civilized world from time to time, and in the seventeenth century, some Dutch traders reported having landed and been subsequently driven from its shores by the native 'savages.' During this century, another Dutchman, Abel Janszoon Tasman discovered an island — once part of the mainland — but now lying off the south coast and known as Tasmania. Nearly two hundred years elapsed, however, before the first white men to settle there reached the Australian shores and, dropping anchor off the south eastern coast, set up a small English colony. The new settlers found themselves in a strange, almost a primeval land, where a vegetation survived which had long since become extinct in other parts of the world; marsupial animals, too, roamed the countryside and an indigenous population, reported to be the most primitive which had yet been discovered on earth, pursued a way of life which was said to be comparable to that of our Palaeolithic Stone Age ancestors in Europe.

As we have seen in a previous chapter, many scientists now agreed that the modern human races, black and white and yellow, though so different superficially, were nevertheless so similar in physical structure that it was presumed that all had descended from a common stock. With the discovery of the Australian aborigines, anthropologists believed that they had found the type most likely to serve as a common ancestor for all races of modern man. These people were said to be 'more primitive' than the most primitive fossil form of modern man then known to have existed in prehistoric Europe, and to have a mean brain capacity of only about 1116 cc.

103

By 1914, many interesting comparisons had been drawn between the cultures of the Australian and Tasmanian aborigines and those of the Palaeolithic and Mesolithic men of Europe. The stone weapons still being used by the aborigines at the end of the nineteenth century were found to resemble the flint implements of Solutrean and later stone age artifacts from France.

The Australian caves were decorated with paintings not unlike those found in the Dordogne country of France and the east coast of Spain, while the coloured pebbles these Australian aborigines used for religious and magical purposes were similar to those which Piette had discovered at Mas d'Azil.

Large numbers of Australian artifacts were now on exhibition in museums, but since many of the forms were still in use when the settlers first arrived in Australia, and as most of them had been collected from surface sites, archaeologists could find no reliable method of distinguishing the contemporary from the more ancient implements. Numerous remains of fossil animals had also been discovered and assigned to the Pleistocene of Australia, but no trace of fossil man or his artifacts had ever been found in association with them.

Intense interest was therefore aroused in scientific circles when it was announced that a fossilized human skull which was assigned "to the Pleistocene, perhaps the early Pleistocene" had been found near Talgai on the Darling Downs in Queensland. The preliminary report was given to the British Association when it met in Sydney, Australia, on August 21st, 1914, by Professors T. W. Edgeworth David and J. T. Wilson.

The Talgai skull had been found by workmen several years previously. No other fossils had been found in association with it, but the bones of extinct animals such as *Diprotodon, Nototherium* and *Megalania* had been obtained from similar formations nearby. The skull, which was said to be that of a young male, corresponded accurately with modern Australian, rather than Tasmanian, skulls. The face was also regarded as being Australian rather than Tasmanian in type. In fact, it was regarded as a prototype Australian who already possessed a brain of modern human size. The Talgai skull was described in a memoir published in 1918 by Mr. A. S. Smith, in which he stressed the need for more data before the anthropological problems which obscured the origins of the Australian and Tasmanian races could be resolved.

Turning next to Africa, it was during this decade that the first important discoveries of fossil man were reported here. Evidence that Stone Age man had lived in Africa had been accumulating for a very long time. As far back as 1867 tools of a Palaeolithic type had been found in Egypt, and while Dubois was working in Java, Professor Peringuay reported the discovery of many stone tools from southern Africa near Cape Town. In the north of Africa too, finds of prehistoric implements, ranging in form from those of Lower Palaeolithic to Upper Palaeolithic, had also been described. It seemed, therefore, that it must only be a matter of time before the remains of fossil man himself would at last be recorded in Africa.

In 1913 Professor Hans Reck, making the first scientific search of the now famous Olduvai Gorge, (then known as the Oldoway Gorge) discovered the remains of a human skeleton, and in 1914, shortly before the outbreak of the First World War, he announced his find to the Berlin Geological Institute. Professor Reck described his find as that of a nearly complete human skeleton, lying in an ultra-contracted position, with the knees drawn right up under the chin. In spite of the fact that this suggested a form of burial, he categorically stated that the "The Oldoway Man" was lying in an undisturbed geological deposit with an "early Pleistocene" fauna. All the teeth were found to be present and Reck records his belief that some of the front ones had been artificially filed, but not in the way found among some present-day African tribes.

Before undertaking a further description of the skull, Reck decided to return to Oldoway for another field season, but while he was on his way to the Gorge his plans were interrupted by the outbreak of the War. He was arrested by the British forces and taken to a prisoner-of-war camp in Egypt, and it was not until the War was over that anything further was heard of his discovery.

Although a full scientific report had not yet been made, the "Oldoway man" received considerable publicity during this decade. Reck's claim regarding the antiquity of the skull was rejected by most scientists, who argued that the skull was no more than that of a modern negro or perhaps a representative of the local Masai tribe, who had somehow been buried into the Pleistocene deposits at Oldoway Gorge.

Meanwhile, just at the outbreak of the War, another fossil human skull, together with a fragment of jaw, was discovered at Boskop, in the Transvaal Province of South

Africa.These Boskop fossil remains, which included some associated limb bone fragments, were unearthed during the course of commercial excavations. Although they were reasonably strongly fossilized, and found in a deposit which was clearly not of very recent age, the precise dating could not be determined.

The skull itself excited a great deal of interest among anatomists because neither in shape, nor in size, did it have any close comparison with those of modern populations in the region. Initial estimates placed its brain capacity at the fantastic figure of 1830 cc. but although this figure was subsequently modified, it was still clear that the brain of Boskop man was far above that of the average modern *Homo sapiens*. Scientific opinion differed greatly, some arguing that it might be an extreme variant of Neanderthal man, others that it resembled one of the early *Homo sapiens* races of Europe, but it was generally considered that interpretations were unwise owing to the incomplete evidence which supported the discovery.

It was also during this decade that Dr. Max Schlosser reported the discovery of the teeth and jaws of three primates in the Oligocene deposits of the Fayoum Depression in Egypt. Scientists of the day were greatly impressed by these fragmentary fossils, as they had come from fossil beds which had already yielded an extensive fauna. Here, at last, was fossil evidence to support Darwin's theory that Africa would prove to be the original home of apes and men.

A few years prior to this discovery, fossil primates from Miocene beds in Europe had shown how slowly the processes of evolution may work, for the Miocene representative of the gibbon family differed only a little from the gibbons of today. This newest discovery from Fayoum revealed that gibbon-like creatures were already evolved in the Upper Oligocene period, and it seemed more than likely, therefore, that they had separated from the common stock at an even earlier date. This evidence of a very great antiquity or the separation of different primate ancestral forms encouraged anatomists of the day, including Keith, to extend the probable date of man's separation from his ape-like cousins to the remote past of the Lower Miocene, or even to the Oligocene geological periods.

It will be interesting to examine a reproduction of the Family Tree of Man, as published by Keith in 1915.

It will be seen that he placed the separation of the gibbons and their fossil ancestors from the stock leading to the greater apes and man, very early in the Oligocene period. He also clearly demonstrates his views that the separation of the family Hominidae from the apes or Pongidae took place in the Upper Oligocene. He suggested that the Family to which we belong today was already fully separated from all our primate cousins by the earliest part of the Miocene period. So strongly does that view disagree with the scientific opinion of the 1950's and 1960's that it needs to be re-stressed today, because, as we shall see in the concluding chapter, it is again being put forward.

The way in which the family tree would now be drawn does not, in fact, differ very greatly from the one which Keith set out in 1915, except in respect of his commentary in terms of time, as shown on the left-hand side of his chart. It will be noted that for Keith in 1915, the Pleistocene period only started 400,000 years ago; the start of the Miocene was less than 2 million years ago; and the Oligocene beginnings a mere 4 million years ago. While modern techniques of dating rocks have completely altered our time concept, modern fossil discoveries have reinforced, rather than changed, Keith's general picture of human evolution.

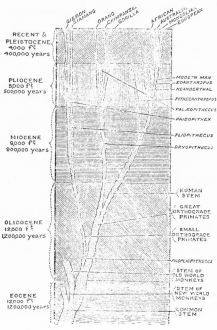

Family Tree of Man, by Sir Arthur Keith, from his book *The Antiquity of Man,* 1915 edition.

CHAPTER IX
1920—1929

By 1920 the reverberations of the War of 1914—1918 were dying away, and with the return to peace-time conditions a widespread and vigorous search was resumed for the fossil remains of ancestral man. Prehistory was now an established branch of science and it was becoming common practice for expeditions to be sponsored by the great scientific institutions and foundations. The standard of field work improved as more funds became available and special new techniques for the excavation and preservation of specimens began to be established. Progress was spectacular and discoveries in Asia, Africa and Europe followed one another in rapid succession. Dubois' discovery of *Pithecanthropus* had greatly strengthened the theory that man was cradled in Asia but, during the decade under review, new evidence was found in Africa which began to make it seem more probable that man's earliest ancestors would ultimately be found in that continent, as Darwin had predicted.

The discoveries were made in three widely separated areas. From East Africa came the news that Dr. L. S. B. Leakey, senior author of the present book, had excavated the remains of relatively recent Stone Age hominids at Nakuru, Elmenteita and Gamble's Cave. Leakey's work proved

110

to be of importance to the story of human evolution, since the uncovering of these prehistoric sites shed new light on the spread of man and his cultures in Africa. "All the world knows," wrote Keith in 1925, "that Sir Arthur Evans . . . restored to Europe a most important chapter which was missing from the early history of her civilization. Mr. Leakey is now doing for Africa what Sir Arthur Evans did for Europe."

In 1921 reports came from Northern Rhodesia that the remains of a hitherto unknown species of hominid had been found in a lead and zinc mine at Broken Hill. Though no fossil human remains had previously come to light in the region, cultural evidence suggesting that early man had once occupied the caves of this district had already been discovered. "Rhodesian Man" was soon being discussed in many parts of the world. The remains, including an almost complete skull, part of a hip bone and two ends of a femur as well as a tibia were not, in the strictest sense of the term, fossilized. They had been protected from disintegration by an incrustation of mineral salts of zinc and lead. In these unusual circumstances any determination of Rhodesian Man's place in the human family had to be based on the anatomical evidence of the bones themselves. The problem was further complicated, as it must always be when anatomists are confronted by a random collection of bones, by the uncertainty as to whether the specimens were, in fact, the remains of a single individual.

Dr. Aleš Hrdlička of the United States was among those who questioned the validity of assuming that the skull and limb bones belonged with each other; five years later the problem was still being debated. By then it had been generally concluded that in brain size and skull characters "Rhodesian Man" was "primitive enough to be placed at the beginning of the Pleistocene, but that he had probably survived long enough to have become contemporary with Neanderthal Man in Europe, to whom, though more simian in aspect, he bore certain resemblances."

Whatever status "Rhodesian Man" was ultimately to be given in the evolutionary story, he nevertheless had the unique distinction of being the first member of an extinct type of man to be unearthed anywhere in Africa.

Finally, in the same way that the remains of "Rhodesian Man" had been discovered, namely as the result of mining operations which were being carried out for commercial purposes, so in 1924 one of the most curious fossil hominids then known to science was brought to light in the limestone quarries of Taung in South Africa. At the request of Professor Raymond Dart of the Witwatersrand University, a colleague, Professor Young, who was visiting the Harts Valley, collected some limestone blocks containing fossil bones from Taung and took them back to Dart. Dart found in these blocks two skulls of a variety of baboon, but he also recovered a brain cast as well as parts of the skull itself and most of the face bones of a "hominid." From these, he carefully reconstructed the head of a little creature which he named *Australopithecus africanus.* The dentition proved to be that of a six-year-old child, and the problems raised by this exciting new skull with its combination of human and simian characters initiated a major and extended scientific controversy. Was *Australopithecus* to be given the status of a man-like ape or an ape-like man? To which stage of the evolutionary story should it be assigned?

The discovery of the Taung skull was made in November of 1924, and by February 1925 Dart had published a preliminary paper in *Nature*. In this paper he claimed that the cranium, dentition, and mandible displayed hominid rather than anthropoid characters, but that while *Australopithecus* was definitely not an ape man like *Pithecanthropus,* neither could he be regarded as belonging to a form ancestral to any living anthropoid ape. In fact, *Australopithecus africanus* seemed to exhibit just those characters which could be expected in "an extinct link between Man and Ape." Since it seemed evident that the skull was not that of a true "true man," Dart announced that he had created a new Family in which the creatures represented by the Taung skull could be accommodated. This he named *Homo-simidae.** It was not long before scientists began to form their own opinions as to the status which should be accorded to *Australopithecus.*

As early as July 1925, Keith wrote in *Nature* that Dart's discovery "threw new light on the history of the anthropoid apes but not on man," and further maintained that *Pithecanthropus* (Java Man) still remained the only known link between man and ape. This seems to have been the general opinion of scientists outside South Africa throughout this post-war decade. In 1930, Sir Grafton Elliot Smith speaks of *Australopithecus* as "an ape about the same size

---

* *Homo-simidae* is no longer recognized by science as a Family.

as *Dryopithecus* but with a closer affinity to Man." Keith, writing (1925) in *New Discoveries of the Antiquity of Man,* in which he devoted six chapters to a detailed discussion of the Taung skull, assumed that it "sprang from the same phylum as the gorilla and the chimpanzee with whom it shared so many features."

Those who subscribed to Dart's theory that *Australopithecus* represented a link between the apes and man regarded the discovery of the Taung skull as important evidence in favour of Darwin's prophecy that man's origins would be found in Africa. Fresh data which were shortly to strengthen the belief of those who favoured Asia as man's birthplace were reported at this stage from the Far East. In 1924 Dubois surprised the scientific world by releasing information about other specimens of the *Pithecanthropus* type which he had found thirty years earlier. In order to try to understand why this material was not made available at the time of its discovery, it is necessary to look at the circumstances surrounding his first announcement of the Java skull cap, femur and teeth. Dubois, as we have seen in Chapter III, believed that these specimens belonged to a single individual, and he had released them first, as being the most important of his finds. There can be little doubt that he expected the scientific world to hail his discovery as "The Missing Link." Instead, his first announcements about *Pithecanthropus* had been quickly followed by controversies and also doubts about the association of the skull with the femur. It seems that he was embittered by this reception and consequently locked away his other hominid fossils and kept them to himself. It was not until

114

Henry F. Osborn and Aleš Hrdlička chanced to hear of them in 1923 that he was persuaded to tell the scientific world of his other discoveries. Thus, in 1924, Dubois first discussed once again the skull cap, femur and teeth from Trinil and stressed that in spite of certain simian characters, *Pithecanthropus* was essentially human. At the same time he released information about an important fragment of a mandible which he had discovered in 1891 at Kedung Brubus, some thirty miles from the more famous Trinil site. He claimed that this jaw fragment came from a stratum of the same geological age as that which yielded his main *Pithecanthropus* specimens and should be attributed to the same genus and species.

Many scientists, including Hans Weinert of Berlin who had previously carried out extensive studies of the Java material, inclined to the belief that the new mandible was too human in its morphology to be attributed to *Pithecanthropus*. This interpretation was strongly contested by Dubois and his supporters.

Now that additional material from Java had been made available, several new reconstructions of Java Man were attempted, the most notable being that of Dr. J. H. McGregor of the American Museum of Natural History. He estimated that *Pithecanthropus* had possessed a brain equal in capacity to that of the smallest representatives of the most primitive living race then known — the Australian aborigines. Scientific opinion regarding the status of *Pithecanthropus* now began to undergo a considerable change. The old views that the Trinil fossils represented an intermediate form between man and ape, or a giant form of extinct

115

gibbon, were no longer tenable, and a belief in the essential humanity of Java Man began to be emphasized.

In August of 1925, parts of a human skull which came to be known as the "Galilee Skull" were found by Mr. Turville-Petre in the Robbers' cave near the shores of Lake Galilee in Israel. They came from the deepest part of the palaeolithic stratum near the mouth of the cave, in association with the fossilized bones of animals, and the stone implements of a former human occupation. In spite of prolonged and patient searching, the missing parts of the "Galilee Skull" were never found and no other fragment of human bone was brought to light at this time.

Applying the same system of chronology to the Robbers' cave as that which had been worked out from the European caves, many prehistorians found it safe to regard the individual represented by the "Galilee Skull" as a variant of the Neanderthal species who had lived during the long period known as the "Mousterian." This important discovery threw new light on the history and distribution of *Homo neanderthalensis.* It had already been established that Neanderthal man had occupied many parts of Europe during Palaeolithic times, but, although his cultures had been found along the African shores of the Mediterranean, his remains had not been previously discovered outside Europe. It still had to be determined whether the Mousterian culture had originated in Europe and spread eastwards to Israel and the Near East, or whether it had been derived from some different and earlier source in Asia. Those who believed that the answer to the problem would be found in Asia, where the origin of man would ultimately be unveiled, were in a majority.

116

Meanwhile, research into Asia's prehistoric past was also being conducted in China. A young Swedish scientist, Dr. J. Gunnar Anderson, who was attached to the Chinese Geological Survey, was investigating some vast limestone caverns at Choukoutien which had already yielded many fossils of animals no longer living in China. At the same time Father Pierre Teilhard de Chardin was exploring the löess covered plateau of Ordos. In 1923 the results of both these field projects were made known at a meeting which was held at the Peking Union Medical College, China. Father Teilhard, who had been sent to China by the Institut de Paléontologie of France, reported on his discoveries on the Ordos plateau. In a deep valley cut by a tributary of the River Hanoi, the priest said he had found and explored a well-marked and complex layer of stone tools and broken bones similar to those with which he had become familiar during his work in the caves of France.

Dr. Anderson then gave a report on the results of his work (in which he had been assisted by Dr. Zdansky). He concluded by announcing the astounding news that when sorting the fossils from the site, which had been assigned to the very early Pleistocene, Zdansky had found two molars of human type which he had identified as *Homo sp.* The teeth were handed over for examination to Dr. Davidson Black, the young Canadian anatomist who was in charge of the Anatomy Department of the College, and at once plans were discussed for raising funds for further investigation. These were eventually made available by the Rockefeller Foundation, and in 1927 a well-equipped expedition reached Choukoutien to put into operation one of the most extensive excavation projects which had been undertaken in the search for early man at this time.

The field party was international in character. It was headed by Professor C. Li, a Chinese geologist and Dr. Birgir Bohlin of Sweden; they were joined from time to time by Davidson Black, by Dr. George Barbour, the English geologist (now of Cincinnati, U.S.A.), by Teilhard of France and by Pei of China. The work was also visited by many other scientists including Elliot Smith of London.

Northern China was at this time plunged in political chaos, and in addition to the difficulties of the locality in which they worked, the members of the expedition were in constant danger from bandits engaged in fierce guerilla skirmishes. Work, however, was carried on with zest, and at the close of the first season, three days before the winter weather would have made further digging impossible, another tooth of hominid type was exposed on the surface of the excavation area. It was carefully extricated and taken to Davidson Black in Peking for examination. It proved to be a beautifully preserved left lower molar, and on the basis of the geological evidence it was assigned to a period "not later than Upper Pleistocene, not earlier than Lower Pleistocene" (as then defined).

Writing in *Nature* in November of 1927 Davidson Black said "the newly discovered specimen displays in the detail of its morphology a number of interesting and unique characters, sufficient, it is believed, to justify the proposal of a new hominid genus *Sinanthropus* to be represented by this material." Thus, on the evidence of a single molar, Davidson Black confidently created a new genus of man. He named it *Sinanthropus pekinensis* — Peking Man, or "The Man of China." For the next three seasons work proceeded at Choukoutien under the leadership of Pei, and once again, just as the winter of 1929 began to make further excavations impossible, an almost complete skull of *Sinanthropus* was uncovered. It was taken from the matrix, dried and transported to Peking by Pei himself. Davidson Black wrote later "that it was entirely due to his skill and devotion that the skull reached safety without loss of a single fragment."

The examination of the skull confirmed the former hypothesis made on the evidence of the single molar. Jubilant, Davidson Black wrote to his friend Keith to say he was thankful that "the foundation of a new genus on the strength of the dental characters has been justified."

The discovery of *Sinanthropus* was ranked in importance with those of Java Man, Rhodesian Man, Piltdown Man, Neanderthal Man and Heidelberg Man. It aroused great excitement in scientific as well as popular circles, and opinions were soon being formed as to what part "Pekin Man" might have played in the evolutionary story.

Some anatomists placed Peking Man's emergence from the phylogenetic tree in between *Pithecanthropus* and *Homo neanderthalensis*. Elliot Smith expressed the view that "*Sinanthropus* was in the intermediate stage between chimpanzee and man. Mentally it had already crossed the human threshold." In his opinion the simian and *hominoid* characters which were combined in *Sinanthropus* afforded corroboration for the belief that the remains found at Piltdown represented "one and the same creature — a very primitive man." The discovery of *Sinanthropus* renewed the still smouldering Piltdown controversy, and strengthened the conviction of those who were inclined to the belief that *Eoanthropus* was the early Pleistocene ancestor of modern man.

In 1926 yet another contribution was added to the Neanderthal story by discoveries in the Devil's Tower Shelter at Gibraltar. An archaeological expedition under the leadership of Miss Dorothy Garrod of Cambridge was responsible for finding five parts of a Neanderthaloid skull of a young child. Stone implements of the Mousterian culture were also recovered as well as the bones and skulls of many species of animal and bird. These included red deer, brown bear, wolf, seal and great auk. The study of the culture and fauna resulted in the assignment of the Gibraltar child to a later part of the same period as that in which the Ehringsdorf skull (see below) had been placed.

This discovery provided very valuable data for the work of the anatomists on the physical growth changes in Neanderthal man, for there were now three skulls available for comparison — this infant of Gibraltar, the child found at La Quina, and the immature youth of Le Moustier.

In 1925 a fragment of what became known as the "London" or "Lloyds" skull was found during building operations in the City of London. In addition to red deer and wild ox a cold climate fauna was embedded in the same deposit and included parts of a mammoth, and what were claimed to be those of a woolly rhinoceros. The skull was described in *Nature* on November 7th, 1925 by Elliot Smith, who stressed that while its characters exhibited some similarity to those of *Homo neanderthalensis,* the visible differences excluded all possibility of assigning the skull to that species. He suggested the possibility that this strange creature might be the representative of a variant who had persisted in the arctic conditions then prevailing in the Thames valley long after Neanderthal man had disappeared from the rest of Europe.

The "London" skull, which was generally assigned to a late phase of the Pleistocene period, was compared by a few scientists with the "Piltdown" skull, and regarded as belonging, therefore, to an older geological horizon.

In 1925, at the time when Turville-Petre was excavating the Galilee Skull, a Neanderthal type of cranium was blasted from a limestone quarry in the little village of Ehringsdorf near Weimar, in the heart of Germany. The Ehringsdorf skull, together with the remains of a prehistoric hearth, was found in a block of stone from the same geological deposit as that in which man-made tools and fossil animal remains had been recovered in a neighboring quarry in 1916. The tools were described as pre-Mousterian, and the deposit assigned to the period preceding the Würm glaciation, or the Mid-Pleistocene (as then defined). The faunal evidence supported this determination, for in addition to red deer, bison, and aurochs, it included both the warm climate *Rhinoceros mercki* and *Elephas antiquus,* which became extinct and disappeared from Europe before the onset of the last glaciation.

A reconstruction of the crushed and flattened parts of the "Ehringsdorf skull" was made by Professor Weidenrich who found that the brain case had received five blows "from some hard object," and furthermore that it had been broken open while the bone was still fresh. This information supported the theory suggested by the broken skulls found at Krapina, that Neanderthal man had practiced cannibalism and eaten human brains.

Previous examples of Neanderthal skulls had all exhibited relatively low roofed vaults, but that of the immature individual found at Ehringsdorf was described as being exceedingly lofty. From this as well as from other morphological evidence it was suggested that, although this was geologically the earliest known representative of the Neanderthal race, the skull was definitely not the most "primitive" in character.

Until this important discovery was made the remains of Neanderthal man had only been found in caves and rock shelters. From the geological and faunal evidence associated with the Ehringsdorf skull, however, it appeared that this early Neanderthal type must have lived in open fertile country during the temperate period which prevailed before the Würm Glaciation set in.

* * *

The important discoveries reviewed so far in this decade were all made in the Old World. The prehistoric past of the New World was still an enigma, for none of the problems concerning early man on the American continent had been solved. In the opinion of Aleš Hrdlička and many other eminent American scientists, none of the human remains which had been found in either North or South America had indicated a type of man materially different from that represented by the American Indians.

122

In 1923 an expedition was sent by the American Museum of Natural History, New York, to examine the Pleistocene fauna which was known to be embedded in a stratum of volcanic ash, high in the Andean region of Ecuador. Near the little village of Punin, the explorers found a female human skull which lay in the same deposit as that which had yielded the remains of the extinct Andean horse, camel and mastodon — an animal which only died out in America some 10,000 years ago. Thus, compared with the other discoveries which have been discussed in this chapter, the Punin skull is a relatively young fossil.* It was described by Louis R. Sullivan and Milo Hellman of the American Museum of Natural History, who both maintained that it bore numerous resemblances to the skulls of the native women of Australia. The possibility was suggested that an Australoid invasion of America in late Pleistocene times might have taken place.

---

* In view of recent discoveries in America, it would seem that this skull fully deserves to be re-investigated.

CHAPTER X
1930—1939

From the cultural evidence which was now available from South Africa and Europe, the belief was gaining ground that there had been some relationship between these two continents in the remote past. Geological research had demonstrated that there had been no physical barriers to prevent such contacts during certain parts of the Pleistocene, for the great Sahara desert, which now cuts off the northern region of Africa, was at one time a fertile land inhabited by man and animals of many kinds. The tendency was to assume that the people now inhabiting Africa had drifted southwards across the Sahara, and that the ancestral remains of such tribes as the Bushman would eventually be found in the Mediterranean area.

In 1930 a discovery was made at Fish Hoek in South Africa which threw a new light upon the ancestry of the Bushman and pointed, as Keith suggested, "to South Africa as the evolutionary cradle of the Bushman type." "Fish Hoek" man was found fifteen miles south of Cape Town, in the Skildergatt cave near Fish Hoek on False Bay. This cave, set high on a sandstone cliff near a good fresh spring as well as close to the sea shore, had attracted the attention of two amateur archaeologists, B. Peers and his son, who

124

felt that it was the sort of place in which early stone age man might have made a home. Preliminary explorations confirmed their hopes and in 1927 they organized a systematic investigation, which they pursued for several years with scientific support. Below a modern stratum which covered the floor of the cave, they found a deposit of marine shells, and below this a thick stratum which was assigned to the Pleistocene. Within it there was evidence of what was already recognized in South Africa as the "Stillbay Culture." In the deepest part of this stratum, they found the skeleton of a small adult male, approximately 5' 1" in height, who had clearly been given some form of ritual burial. Stone tools, belonging to the Stillbay culture, which were at that time considered to resemble those of the "Mousterian" cultures of Europe, had already been found in several regions of Africa, and this had therefore tentatively suggested that when the remains of "Stillbay Man" were found, they might possibly exhibit Neanderthaloid characters. It came as a surprise to many anatomists, therefore, when the remains from Skildergatt cave, which were examined by Professor M. R. Drennan of Cape Town University, proved to be those of a prototype Bushman. This find supported Keith's previously published theory that the Bushman type had evolved in South Africa, where this race is found today.

The brain capacity of "Fish Hoek" man was estimated at 1600 cc., but was clearly smaller than that of Boskop man. The skull was said to be remarkable for its extension backwards behind the ears. In spite of the large size of the skull, however, "Fish Hoek" man was found to have had a small face and teeth resembling those of the modern Bushman. When discussing this discovery, Keith commented on the fact that, in spite of the large brain capacity of this prototype Bushman, the race had apparently been unable to save itself from the extinction to which it seems to be heading today. He concluded that the size of the brain should not necessarily be regarded as an indication of mental ability.

While Peers and his son were excavating the Skildergatt cave in South Africa, Dorothy Garrod, who had now joined the British School of Archaeology in Jerusalem, was investigating a limestone cave at Shukbah, situated on the eastern slopes of the Judaean Hills, midway between the River Jordan and the Mediterranean Sea. Massive blocks of fallen limestone had disturbed the deposits in this cave, but in the hard breccia beneath them, the excavators recovered a number of fossil human bones, in association with stone tools resembling the Mousterian culture. Among the fossils, Dorothy Garrod found a molar tooth which was reported to belong to an individual of the Neanderthal type. This find thus supported Turville-Petre's claim that Neanderthal man had once occupied Palestine.

Tentative trenching had also been conducted in some of the caves in the limestone cliffs on the eastern slopes of Mount Carmel, which rises behind the Bay of Acre to the north of Shukbah. In 1928 the destruction of these caves, including the vast limestone cavern of Athlit, was threatened as a result of several commercial developments. At this point, the Department of Antiquities of the Government of Israel invited the British School of Archaeology in

Jerusalem to help them. Dorothy Garrod was accordingly recalled from Shukbah and invited to undertake an excavation. A long succession of strata was exposed in the Athlit cave during the course of her excavations. These clearly indicated that it had been occupied by man for a long period of time. In the deepest stratum of all, Dorothy Garrod found (as she had at Shukbah and as Turville-Petre had in the Robbers' cave at Galilee) sufficient evidence to prove that the cave had been used in Palaeolithic times by Neanderthal man. Above this, in successive occupation layers, she recovered evidence of cultures which she assigned to early, middle, and upper Aurignacian.

Dorothy Garrod, later joined by Dr. Theodore McCown, investigated several other caves at Mount Carmel, including Tabūn and Shūl, where numerous human fossils were uncovered. In 1933 some of the blocks of matrix were transported from Israel to The Royal College of Surgeons in London, where for the next two and a half years, the task of developing out the fossils was undertaken. Descriptions of the Mount Carmel cultural material were published by Dorothy Garrod while Keith and McCown made extensive studies of the human remains.

It was claimed that the skulls and skeletons revealed an extraordinary "mosaic" of Neanderthaloid and Cromagnon characters. "It is possible," wrote Keith, "that Neanderthal and Cromagnon — Palaeoanthropic and Neanthropic — stocks had met on the flanks of Mount Carmel in Mid-Pleistocene times, and that the fossil bones described here represent the progeny of their union. We have given the supposition of hybridity our serious consideration and have rejected it." It seemed more likely to him that a site had been uncovered where evolutionary changes were taking place in both the Neanderthal and Cromagnon stocks.

In 1931 Leakey organized his third East African Expedition. This time it had as its target the Oldoway Gorge*, where Hans Reck had worked before World War I, and sites on the southern shores of Kavirondo Gulf of Lake Victoria in Kenya. Leakey has always been the first to admit that the element of chance often plays a leading part in discoveries of fossil remains. Nevertheless, there is nothing haphazard about the methods he employs in his investigations. In *Adam's Ancestors* Leakey stressed the importance of studying what he calls the "Prehistoric Geography and the Prehistoric Climate" of any area which is selected for research. A few years later, when discussing the two highly controversial discoveries made at Kanjera and Kanam by the Third East African Archaeological Expedition, Leakey's "luck" was described somewhat differently by Dr. Robert Broom of Pretoria Museum. "Dr. Leakey," he wrote, "with the restlessness of the true hunter, is always looking for something new, and with the intuition of true genius, generally looking in the right spot."

At Kanjera, Leakey was mainly aiming at the recovery of fossil animal remains in association with the tools of the hand-axe culture, but the site he chose for the 'dig' proved 'lucky.' Fragments of three human fossil skulls were recovered. Similarly at Kanam, where the search for an early Pleistocene fauna was proving highly successful, one of his

---

* Now Olduvai.

staff, Juma Gitau, made a very important discovery of a fossil human jaw fragment.

The fossil human skulls from Kanjera were mainly represented by fragments found on the surface, but when excavations were carried out, two small fragments that fitted the surface specimens were found *in situ*. As a result of detailed studies a reconstruction of the fragments of the two more complete skulls, Leakey claimed that they represented an early primitive *Homo sapiens* who lived at the end of the Mid-Pleistocene.

Leakey's study of the Kanam mandible was made difficult by the fact that during life the individual had fractured his jaw, and the subsequent healing process had obscured some of the anatomy. The specimen itself was, moreover, encased in an exceedingly hard matrix. At the end of his study Leakey suggested that the Kanam mandible exhibited features recalling *Homo sapiens,* but with certain major differences. He therefore proposed to call it *Homo kanamensis,* and regarded it as "an ancestor and not a cousin of *Homo sapiens* who had lived in Africa in the Lower Pleistocene." In 1933 a conference attended by many distinguished anthropologists was held in Cambridge to discuss these two discoveries. It unanimously decided to support Leakey's claims.

It was not long, however, before the authenticity of the geological ages of the discoveries was hotly contested by Professor P. G. H. Boswell, who maintained that they had been washed into an older deposit by erosion and were therefore of a younger geological age than that claimed for them by Leakey. The conflicting views of these two men were widely discussed and it was decided, in the end, to put both the Kanam mandible and the Kanjera skulls into a 'suspense account' for the time being.

In 1933, the remains of a human skull which were to throw new light on the ancestry of Neanderthal man, were found at Steinheim, Germany, some twenty miles north of Stüttgart. The circumstances of the discovery were similar to those in which the Heidelberg jaw had been found, for the skull was first seen by the owner of a gravel pit who was keenly interested in prehistoric remains. The find was immediately reported by Herr Sigrist to Professor Berkhemer of the Stüttgart Natural History Museum, who hurried to the spot. Work at the gravel pit had already exposed a stratum containing a cold climate fauna, and below this, in association with a typical warm climate fauna which included *Rhinoceros mercki* and *Elephas antiquus,* lay the "Steinheim skull." It was extracted from the matrix by Berkhemer himself. Since there was considerable doubt as to whether the deposit in which it was embedded had been formed during the second or third inter-glacial phase, it was assigned loosely to "The Pleistocene Age."

The skull, which was long and narrow, lacked the mandible, part of the left side of the face and the surrounding occipital foramen. It was believed to represent a young female. It presented many interesting and curious features, for while the prominent brow ridges and strongly built upper jaw resembled *Homo neanderthalensis* in some respects, the back part of the skull was rounded, as in modern man. The brain capacity of "Steinheim man" was estimated by Berkhemer to be 1070 cc. In his opinion this fossil represented an individual who was older in geological time as well as more primitive than Neanderthal man, and yet approximated in many features to *Homo sapiens*.

This view was opposed by many anthropologists and various theories were postulated in an attempt to explain the problems presented by the Steinheim skull. Dr. Hans Weinert of Berlin maintained that it should be grouped unquestionably with the Neanderthal skulls, and suggested that the modern characters which it exhibited could be attributed to the retention of childlike traits, due to the fact that the skull was said to be that of a female. Others who believed that inter-breeding had probably taken place among the different races of early man, suggested that Steinheim man was an example of an offspring of Neanderthal and *sapiens* parents.

Reviewing the discovery a few years later, Sir Wilfred Le Gros Clark of the Department of Anatomy of Oxford University believed that in general the Steinheim skull suggested an "anatomical link between the ancient *Pithecanthropus* and *Homo sapiens,* though approximating much more closely to the latter." Leakey, when writing of the importance of the Steinheim discovery in *Adam's Ancestors,* stressed his view that, while the skull exhibited many similarities to the more typical Neanderthal skulls, it was "markedly less specialized, both in respect of the face and of the skull itself," and thus confirmed his belief that the Neanderthal type was "the product of over-specialization away from the common stem which gave rise to *Homo sapiens.*" Leakey suggested, therefore, that such extinct hominids as Neanderthal man and Rhodesian man should no longer be regarded as 'primitive stages' of modern man, but rather as over specialized off-shoots from *Homo sapiens.*

At Swanscombe in the Thames Valley, England, (not far from Galley Hill where the skeleton of 'Galley Hill Man' was found in 1888) thousands of Chellean and Acheulean flint implements and innumerable fossil animal bones were still being recovered from the local gravel pits. Workmen employed to dig these pits at Swanscombe had for many years past been taught by anxious prehistorians how to recognize stone age tools and had been urged to keep a sharp look-out for any fossil human remains which might turn up. In 1935, two years after the discovery in the gravel pit at Steinheim, the long awaited fossil remains of man were found in the Barnfield Pit at Swanscombe. In this case the whim of chance played an important part in the discovery, for it was only by a fortunate coincidence that a dentist Mr. A. T. Marston, happened to pay one of his regular visits to the Barnfield Pit on the very day that the fossil fragment was exposed. He recognized it at once as belonging to a human skull. The fossil, which but for Marston's timely arrival might have been lost to science, proved to be a human occipital bone in a good state of preservation and showing no signs of posthumous distortion.

A preliminary notice of this famous find appeared in *Nature* in October of 1935, and during the months that followed a constant survey was made of the gravel face of the pit as it was worked back. In 1936 Marston's search was rewarded. A few yards away from the place where the first discovery was made, and in the same level of the gravel deposit, he came upon a left parietal which articulated perfectly with the occipital. The skull fragments, which were associated with stone hand axes of the Acheulean culture as well as teeth and bones of a warm climate fauna including *Elephas antiquus* and red deer, were assigned to the Great Inter-glacial or Mindel Riss period.

In view of the extreme importance of the discovery, and at Marston's suggestion, the Swanscombe skull was subsequently investigated by a Research Committee appointed by the Royal Anthropological Institute. The members included Le Gros Clark, Dr. Kenneth P. Oakley, Mr. A. C. Hinton and others. In their joint publication in 1938 the members of this committee reported their unanimous decision that the Swanscombe skull was "an indigenous fossil of the 100 foot Terrace of the Lower Thames."

Le Gros Clark, who reported on the *General Features of the Swanscombe Skull Bones,* regarded them as belonging to a female who had died in her early twenties, and estimated the brain capacity as 1325 cc. In his opinion the only feature which distinguished the skull from those of modern man was the extreme thickness of the bones, though he did not ignore the possibility that evidence of some differentiation might occur in the missing parts. Summarizing his studies of the Swanscombe skull, he emphasized that the main point of interest of the bones lay in the indication they gave that, in Early Palaeolithic times, "the human brain had already acquired a status typical of *Homo sapiens.*" The members of the Committee concluded their joint report on the Swanscombe skull by announcing their decision that it should be regarded as a representative of Acheulian man who had lived in the Mindel-Riss Interglacial period.

The discovery was at once widely discussed and contrasts were drawn between the Swanscombe skull and those of Java man and Neanderthal man. Inevitably, owing to the similar thickness of the bones, comparisons were also made with that of "Piltdown man." It was generally agreed that the Swanscombe skull bones approximated much more closely to those of *Homo sapiens* but there was some support for the theory that it might be a descendant from the Piltdown group.

The prophesies of such great thinkers as Keith, Boule and Elliot Smith that man's origins would be found in the Pliocene or even in the Miocene, were at this time regarded by many scientists as "wild conjectures." The conclusions reached by the Swanscombe committee therefore, that a hominid with a highly evolved brain had lived as long ago as the Mindel-Riss Interglacial, postulated an antiquity for man which many of them were not prepared to accept.

Further search in the Barnfield Pit did not reveal any additional evidence of Acheulian man at this time, and the problems posed by the Swanscombe skull and the comparable discoveries made by Leakey at Kanam and Kanjera remained unsolved.

The search for early man was meanwhile being pursued with great vigor in the Far East, where an expedition under the leadership of Professor von Koenigswald was carrying out extensive explorations of the Djetis deposits in Java. These deposits were assigned to the Lower Pleistocene and were reported as of an older geological age than those at Trinil which had yielded the original *Pithecanthropus* material in 1891. By 1939 a number of fossils (all now attributed to *Pithecanthropus*) had been brought to light and were available for study. Apart from the original Trinil fossils found by Dubois, there were now fragments of four different skulls — referred to as *Pithecanthropus* skulls II, III, IV and *Pithecanthropus modjokertensis,* a juvenile skull — as well as a mandible and a maxilla.

Von Koenigswald believed that he had discovered the remains of three distinct types of humanity in the Djetis deposits, two of which he placed into the genus *Pithecanthropus* and accorded them distinct specific rank — *Pithecanthropus modjokertensis* and *Pithecanthropus dubius.* The former of these two species is now regarded as no more than a *Pithecanthropus erectus* child. The jaw of the third type of humanity recognized by von Koenigswald and named *Meganthropus palaeojavanicus* showed a number of essentially human characters in spite of its great size, and was described as being within the direct line leading to man. His views were contested by many scientists, who did not think that the evidence justified his decision to create a new genus for this "giant" jaw. Leakey, when discussing this discovery in 1953, suggested that it should be regarded as a highly specialized "side branch which broke away from that leading to modern man, and eventually became extinct, just as *Pithecanthropus* did."

Another valuable but puzzling contribution to the story of early man in Asia was made when the Geological Survey were working at Ngandong, which lies on the Solo River, Java. Between 1931 and 1941 the remains of at least eleven skulls were recovered from a terrace deposit which was assigned to the Upper Pleistocene, and therefore of a younger geological age than the site which had yielded the Trinil remains. The skulls, which all lacked the facial skeleton, exhibited massive brow ridges and well developed muscular crests on the occipital bone; the average brain capacity was estimated as ranging between 1150 and 1300 cc. Only one limb bone (a tibia) was found in association with the skulls, and this was described as resembling those of modern man.

The individuals represented by this rich find were first described by Dr. W. F. F. Oppenoorth, who named them *Javanthropus soloensis,* but there was considerable discussion at the time as to whether the fossils were, in fact, sufficiently distinctive in type to warrant the creation of a separate species to accommodate them. Many suggestions were put forward at a later date in order to try and solve the problems presented by this discovery. Le Gros Clark inclined to the belief that Solo man was a variant of the Neanderthal stock; von Koenigswald that Solo man filled the gap between the *Pithecanthropus — Sinanthropus* and *Neanderthalensis* groups, Weidenreich suggested that *Homo soloensis* was probably derived from *Pithecanthropus,* and developed ultimately (probably through a Neanderthaloid stage) into *Homo sapiens.* In Leakey's view, as expressed in the 1953 edition of *Adam's Ancestors,* Solo man should be regarded as a late survivor of *Pithecanthropus.* Until new data become available, Solo man's place in the story of human evolution cannot be established.

There seems to have been a general belief at this time that some relationship existed between *Sinanthropus* and *Pithecanthropus,* but none as to whether one was more "primitive" than the other. Anatomists suggested that it was possible for *Pithecanthropus* to have retained a "primitive" character in one of his structures, while *Sinanthropus* did so in another, and that the two were probably related to one another in much the same way as the races of man are today." Many of them believed that the minor structural differences between *Pithecanthropus* and *Sinanthropus* could have been effected by racial deviation or were due to the effects of environment. Other anatomists began to suggest that Pekin man (*Sinanthropus*) was no more than a distant species of Java man (*Pithecanthropus*) and should be called *Pithecanthropus pekinensis*.

In 1935 the remains of an extinct type of man were found by Dr. Kohl-Larsen on the eastern shores of Lake Eyasi in Tanganyika, East Africa. They were first described by Weinert of Germany who inclined to the belief that they were of an older geological age than the Upper Pleistocene (to which they were later assigned by Leakey). A good deal of controversy arose over the status to be accorded to this interesting fossil, for while Weinert regarded it as belonging to a "primitive" hominid, Leakey believed that it was a "very highly specialized" type. Some years later, when discussing the Eyasi skull in *Adam's Ancestors,* Leakey suggested that since it resembled the skulls of Java man and Pekin man more closely than those of either Neanderthal or Rhodesian man, it should be regarded as of the same genus as the Far Eastern skulls, a distinct species of *Pithecanthropus.*

A new and important series of discoveries which eventually influenced opinion regarding the status to be accorded to *Australopithecus* was being made in South Africa at this time. In 1936 Robert Broom visited some caves at Sterkfontein some thirty miles from Johannesburg. The breccia of these caves which had already been quarried for many years, had yielded a number of fossil animal remains, and it was believed that a great many more which might have proved of inestimable value to science must have been destroyed during commercial operations. On this occasion part of the brain case of a skull was handed by Mr. Brownlow, the supervisor of the quarries, to Broom. He immediately set to work to search for more and eventually recovered many additional fragments of the skull, which he identified as that of an adult primate. He claimed that it was of a form allied to *Australopithecus africanus* which Dart had discovered in 1925, but he named it *Australopithecus transvaalensis*. After further consideration of his discovery, however, he decided to accord it full generic rank and renamed it *Plesianthropus transvaalensis*. Accounts of the new skull appeared in many parts of the world, and the popular press hailed it with the now familiar type of headings — "A New Ancestral Link between Ape and Man," and "Missing Link Found."

It was not until he had completed a lecture tour in America, where much interest was shown in his discovery, that Broom again visited Sterkfontein and was handed another skull fragment by Brownlow. Inquiries elicited the information that it had been picked up by a schoolboy about two miles away, at Kromdraai. Broom hurried across the valley to Kromdraai and located the schoolboy, who showed him where he had found the skull, and also handed him other parts of the same skull and some teeth. When the Kromdraai skull had been restored, Broom considered that it exhibited so many differences from the Sterkfontein specimen that he decided to make it the type of another new genus and species. He therefore named it *Paranthropus robustus*.

Scientific opinion was very critically opposed to Broom's decision to create a new genus for each of his discoveries. He claimed, however, that the geological deposits as well as the fauna associated with the two discoveries were very different, and therefore it should not be surprising to find that the "ape men" from the two sites exhibited structural differences. "There is nothing remarkable," he wrote, "in finding three different genera of 'ape men' in the Transvaal," and went on to prophecy that probably even more genera would be discovered in this area in the years to come.

The studies of available fossil material and the hunt for new evidence of the Australopithecines of South Africa continued until 1939 when the world-wide search for early men came to an abrupt stop as the peoples of the world were plunged once more into major war.

CHAPTER XI
1940—1949

In September of 1939 Great Britain declared war on Germany and one by one the countries of Europe were engulfed in a major conflict which was waged on land and sea and in the air for the next five years. In the Far East, however, an uneasy peace prevailed until the end of 1941, and work was continued at the famous Choukoutien site in China, as well as in Java where von Koenigswald found another mandible of the *Meganthropus palaeojavanicus* type.

This massive jaw, which was described by von Koenigswald as being essentially human in spite of its "giant" proportions, was found near the site from which *Pithecanthropus modjokertensis* (the *Pithecanthropus* child) had been recovered from the Lower Pleistocene deposits at Sangiran. The two pre-molars and the molar tooth which were preserved in this jaw fragment were described as bearing certain resemblances to those of "Pekin Man" as well as to the South African "near men" — the Australopithecines. The rudimentary beginnings of the *spina mentalis* (the small outgrowth of bone to which certain tongue muscles are attached) were present in the mandible and it was claimed that *Meganthropus palaeojavanicus*, like Pekin man and Heidelberg man, must have possessed the physical means of articulate speech. The evidence afforded by this second "giant" mandible still failed to convince most authorities that von Koenigswald had sufficient justification for separating *Meganthropus palaeojavanicus* from *Pithecanthropus*.

In December of 1941, after the fierce attack on Pearl Harbor by Japanese bombers, the United States declared war on Japan, and the search for prehistoric man in Asia also came to an abrupt end. Java was occupied by Japanese troops who had been ordered to confiscate all the *Pithecanthropus* material. Casts of the fossils were hastily made and substituted (where possible) for the originals, which were then hidden by von Koenigswald's friends. These tactics were highly successful, and when von Koenigswald was released from captivity after the end of the war, nearly all his *Pithecanthropus* fossils were recovered. The fate of the Choukoutien fossils, on the other hand, is still a mystery. Weidenreich, who succeeded Davidson Black at the Peking Medical College, left China for America at the outbreak of war, and in spite of all the efforts to save them, the *Sinanthropus* fossils were apparently either destroyed by hostile forces or lost on the way to America. Fortunately for science, descriptions of many of the fossils had already been published by Davidson Black, and Weidenreich dedicated the remaining years of his life in America to the publication of a series of valuable and outstanding monographs on *Sinanthropus* which he illustrated with many drawings and photographs.

In 1944, while the war was still in progress, Professor S.

Sergi of Rome published an account of the discovery of the two skulls which had been found at Saccopastore, Italy, as far back as 1929 and 1935 respectively. The remains had been recovered from the bank of a tributary of the River Tiber, and were found in association with a warm climate fauna, including the remains of hippopotamus and *Elephas antiquus*. It was believed, therefore, that these specimens belonged in time to the last Inter-glacial phase of the Ice Age — the Riss-Würm. The skulls exhibited certain Neanderthaloid characters including a strong development of the supra-orbital ridges, while the dental arcade was similar to that of modern man. In Sergi's opinion, these interesting specimens represented a stage of development between an early Neanderthal man such as Steinheim, and the overspecialized individuals of the same type so often referred to as "Mousterian man."

In 1947, an important discovery was made at Fontechevade near Angoulême in France by Mlle. G. Henri-Martin, daughter of the Henri-Martin whose work at La Quina has won him a lasting place among the pioneers of prehistory. The excavations carried out by Mlle. Henri-Martin yielded a rich collection of fossils and stone tools, as well as additional human remains. Beneath a typical Magdalenian occupation level, an Aurignacian layer followed by a Mousterian living floor were uncovered. Finally, beneath an undisturbed layer of stalagmite, a stratum containing the remains of a skull cap of one individual and a fragment of the frontal of a second was reached. These were associated with a warm climate fauna which included deer, bear, bovids, a rhinoceros and a tortoise similar to the Greek tortoise which is now found in the South Mediterranean area. This level was assigned to the last Inter-glacial phase of the Ice Age — the Riss-Wurm, and contained man-made tools of the type assigned by Abbé Breuil to the Tayacian culture.

In her preliminary report of the discovery to the Académie des Sciences, Mlle. Henri-Martin described the skull bones as being thicker and smaller than those of *Homo sapiens* but of similar shape, and entirely lacking the strongly developed supra-orbital ridges usually associated with "Mousterian man."

The Fontechevade skull fragments, the first of their type to be found in France, were believed to represent the remains of two individuals closely resembling modern man who had inhabited Europe in the "early Pleistocene," probably at the same time as Heidelberg man. There was now a growing belief that these discoveries, as well as those from Ehringsdorf, Steinheim, Swanscombe, Heidelberg and possibly even "Piltdown" might represent an early and generalized form of *Homo neanderthalensis*, and that the many fossils referred to as "Mousterian Man" were typical of an over-specialized and later off-shoot which was already heading towards extinction.

A considerable accumulation of data about the Neanderthal group was now available for study, but although many attempts were made to establish the full story of their progressive development, no theories were postulated that embraced and solved the problems involved. It was now already a hundred years since the type specimen of *Homo neanderthalensis* had been discovered in the Neanderthal cave in 1856, and in the fourth edition of *Adam's Ancestors*

143

Leakey suggested that since so much of the Neanderthal material had been collected at a time when it was all referred to as of "Mousterian times," a re-assessment of the many fossil remains and their associated cultures was now essential and might throw new light on the subject.

In South Africa the search for early man had also come to a standstill during the war years, although many new studies had been made of the available Australopithecine material. In 1946, Broom published a book, *The South African Fossil Ape-Men,* in which he clearly indicated that the South African scientists believed their discoveries in the Transvaal would "probably solve the problem of the origin of man." "Whether the 'ape-men' were regarded as sub-human or human," he said, "they were certainly closely allied to man and not at all nearly related to the living primates. And we may regard it as certain," he went on, "that man arose from a Pliocene member of the Australopithecines probably very close to *Australopithecus africanus* itself. The discovery of these South African ape-men has for the first time thrown definite light on how man arose." The book was well received and now that the adult skulls from Kromdraai and Sterkfontein, as well as the many limb fragments which had been recovered, were available for study, some of the opposition to Dart's interpretation of *Australopithecus africanus,* (particularly that of the English scientists), was now publicly withdrawn.

Keith, whose studies of the Taung child had been seriously handicapped by having to work with inferior casts, now told Broom that he regarded the South African anthropoids as being much more human than he had ori-

144

ginally supposed. "I now agree with you," he wrote, "that that piece of humerus, the lower end of femur, the astragalus, metacarpal, and os magnum, are parts of *Paranthropus* and *Plesianthropus,* that the teeth have all the characters of human teeth, that the hands were free and that the posture was bipedal; and yet I call *Paranthropus* not a man but an anthropoid . . . "

Le Gros Clark, whose views of *Australopithecus africanus* had been similar to those expressed in the first instance by Keith, now underwent a change of opinion after visiting Dart and Broom in South Africa. Instead of regarding the Australopithecines as typical apes, he now believed that they represented a form of creature which approached much more closely to a human ancestor than any other similar form which had then been discovered.

Funds were now urgently needed if the search for fossil man was to be continued in the Transvaal. Fortunately for the South African anthropologists, General Smuts, at that time Prime Minister of South Africa, was deeply interested in the science of prehistory. In a letter to Broom he expressed his own conviction regarding the mystery of human evolution. "I look for something in the nature of the Universe," he wrote, "to account for what has happened, and that something must be both physical and organic and mental, and also much more." In 1946, at his request, the South African Government made generous funds available for prehistoric research, and accordingly Broom set out for Sterkfontein. The site he chose to investigate was near to the one which had yielded the type specimen of *Plesianthropus* and it was not long before a piece of hard breccia was blasted from the cliffside revealing the two halves of an almost complete skull of the same type. It was photographed *in situ,* and descriptions appeared in the *Illustrated London News* as well as in South African and American illustrated publications. Shortly afterwards Broom found a lower jaw, some limb bones and, most important of all, three pelvic bones which clearly indicated that his 'ape-man' had walked 'on his hind legs.' Certain morphological differences, however, were observed between the pelvic bones of *Plesianthropus* and *Homo sapiens,* although the pelvis of *Plesianthropus* was described as "not at all anthropoid," it was believed to be only 85% human." This valuable new evidence caused many of those who still regarded *Plesianthropus* as an ape to change their views.

Many other discoveries were made at Sterkfontein during this period, including two more skulls in good condition, the fragmentary remains of five others, and the lower jaw of a child. This immature specimen was of particular importance to Broom, for after studying its morphology he came to the conclusion that his decision to create a new genus for *Plesianthropus* had been a correct one. *Plesianthropus,* he maintained, though allied to *Australopithecus africanus,* was nevertheless generically distinct.

In 1948 the remains of another 'ape-man' were exposed in one of the caves in the Makapan valley not far from Sterkfontein. Dart described it as resembling *Australopithecus africanus,* and from the associated evidence in the cave was convinced that this 'ape-man' had known how to make fire — a view which was not shared by either Broom or his colleague Dr. J. T. Robinson. Dart named his new find *Australopithecus prometheus.*

In the same year, Broom, financed by the University of California, initiated an investigation at Swartkrans. The new site yielded a number of interesting discoveries including a massive but incomplete jaw of another 'ape-man.' The teeth which were preserved in this specimen were described as being much larger than those of *Homo sapiens,* but nevertheless human in structure. Broom regarded his new discovery as a distinct species of *Paranthropus* and named it *Paranthropus crassidens.* The associated fauna at this site proved to be quite unlike that from the sites at Kromdraai and Sterkfontein, and from the presence of such fossil remains as those of a new type of baboon, a new golden mole, a primitive type of hyena, antelope and dassies, it was suggested at first that the deposit should be assigned to the Pliocene.

The possible importance of 'gigantism' in the story of human evolution now began to attract a certain amount of attention. A new genus had been created by von Koenigswald on the evidence of three huge teeth found in China and named *Gigantopithecus.* He, again had discovered the 'giant jaws' of *Meganthropus javanicus* in Java, and now in South Africa, further evidence of 'gigantism' had been found by Broom. Weidenreich who believed that 'gigantism' might have played an interesting part in human evolution, described it as a "primitive character which has the tendency to diminish as evolution advances." It was suggested that 'gigantism' might perhaps explain the mystery of man's brain, and a theory was postulated that 'ape-man' evolved

147

into 'giant ape-men,' and then diminished in body size while retaining the relatively large brains of their ancestors.

An interesting but puzzling fragment of a jaw was found at this time by Robinson in a pocket of hard brown breccia at Swartkrans. Three well-preserved molars were contained in the jaw and were described as belonging to a "human specimen with Australopithecine affinities." Robinson, supported by Broom, regarded the individual represented by the mandible "as being possibly the oldest known man," and on the slender evidence afforded by the dentition they created a new genus and named it *Telanthropus capensis*.

A very remarkable number of primate fossils had now been recovered from the Transvaal in a short space of time. In general, the scarcity of primate fossil remains is due to the fact that so many of them were forest dwelling creatures. In such a habitat bones have little chance of becoming fossilized as they are soon covered by rotting vegetation and eventually dissolved by the acids of the soil. All the evidence from the Transvaal, however, suggested that the small, lightly built Australopithecines had lived in open country where they had most probably fallen easy prey to hungry carnivores and been dragged into caves where their remains had become fossilized.

It was now of vital importance to try to establish the chronology of the geological deposits from which the various specimens had been taken. The problem was far from easy. The strata in which the 'ape-men' of South Africa had been discovered were formed mostly of hard limestone breccia, and the stratification was so poorly defined that in most cases geological dating had been impossible. Scientists therefore sought to rely on the evidence of associated fauna on which to base their estimates. Again difficulties arose, for many of the associated fossil animal remains which had been assigned to the Pliocene were later believed to represent a fauna which had persisted in the southern half of Africa long after it had become extinct in other regions.

In view of the difficulty of arriving at any precise chronology, geologists had reached a general agreement to assign the Australopithecinae to "an early phase of the Pleistocene." This phase, corresponding to the pre-Acheulian cultural period, had now been defined at the 1948 International Geological Congress in London as the Villafranchian, a term which was gradually adopted by prehistorians.

There was now sufficient evidence regarding the morphology of the Australopithecines for an estimate of the general characters of the group to be attempted, though the specimens were not all believed to have been contemporary. In stature they were shown to be small and lightly built, perhaps resembling the modern Pygmy races. Their average brain capacity was estimated at between 500-700 cc. and was thus roughly half that of modern man. The skulls were described as being smaller, though similar in shape, to those of *Homo sapiens;* the jaws comparatively large, while the teeth were human in their morphology. The limb bones were believed to resemble those of *Homo sapiens* rather than those of any of the great apes, and the pelvic bones had demonstrated clearly that *Australopithecus* walked erect as man does today. It is interesting to note that many scientists of the time found this combination of a small stature with an upright posture so apparently contradictory that they were not able to accept the evidence of the South African fossils.

Scientific opinion was still sharply divided as to whether the South African scientists had been justified in creating so many different genera within the Australopithecine group, though many authorities were now willing to recognize more than one species of the genus. However, Broom remained true to his original decision. "If the Taung cave, he said, "is say 2,000,000 years old, and the Sterkfontein 1,200,000 years, it is most unlikely that the types we now know bridged the gap of 800,000 years."

In the fourth edition of *Adam's Ancestors,* Leakey suggested that "the really important thing about all these different species of 'near-men' is that they *are* 'near-men,' and reveal to us a branch of the ape-human stock of which we have so far no knowledge from elsewhere. Moreover, they provide the most important evidence against the theory that man was derived from some creature in any way resembling the great apes of today."

The problem of classifying the Australopithecines within the Order Primates could not be solved at this time without new evidence, but various theories were postulated in an effort to clarify the position in the light of existing knowledge. Many authorities were prepared to accept that mankind had passed through the stage of development represented by the South African 'near-men,' and some believed that they were in fact directly ancestral to *Homo sapiens.* This latter theory, however, was only tenable for those who believed, as the South African scientists did, that the Australopithecines could be referred to the Pliocene period. To those who assigned them to the Villafranchian, it was clearly not reasonable to suggest that the South African 'near-men' could be ancestral to *Homo sapiens* unless they were regarded as late survivals of a side branch of the ancestral stock leading to man.

The fossil remains of a variety of anthropoid apes of generalized form had now been discovered in the Oligocene, Miocene and Pliocene deposits of many parts of the world. New evidence was badly needed however, to bridge the gap which existed between the records of such ape-like creatures as *Proconsul* of East Africa, *Propliopithecus* from Egypt or *Ramapithecus* from the Siwalik Hills of India, and those which were now being compiled of the 'near-men' of South Africa. Few scientists now doubted that the Hominidae and the Pongidae had evolved from a common stock. The point in time at which the separation had taken place remained unknown.

CHAPTER XII
1950—1959

This decade was one of very considerable importance in respect to the study of human evolution. Discoveries were made which did a great deal to clarify the whole issue of just how man originated.

We have already seen, when dealing with the period 1910—1919 how a discovery reported in Great Britain, from Piltdown in Sussex, caused a major stir among anatomists. The Piltdown skull became the subject of intensive studies and much controversy. The foremost British authority, Keith, led the field in the detailed nature of his investigations. He concluded that the find represented a strange early hominid whose brain capacity had evolved at a much more rapid rate than his jaws and teeth, so that the former had become, to all intents and purposes, like that of the present day man, with the jaws and teeth apparently still very much like those of an ape.

It must be remembered when we consider the events about to be discussed, that the period 1910—1919 was one during which public and scientific opinion was geared to expect to find some kind of "missing link" between apes and man. This was due to the deep-seated view held at that time that man was evolved from an "ape-like creature" using this term to mean something like a chimpanzee. Even in those days a certain number of scientists were unhappy about the views expressed by men like Keith, Smith Woodward and Elliot Smith about the Piltdown find. Some rejected it altogether, others treated it as something that should be held in a "suspense account" until such time as it was confirmed or refuted by other discoveries.

Then in the year 1953, a new method of checking upon fossil human remains in relation to associated animal bones, by means of fluorine tests, was being developed by Dr. K. Oakley. He soon decided to apply this test to the Piltdown skull and mandible, as well as to the fossil animal bones which were supposed to have been associated with the human ones. The result of these early tests was very interesting. He reported that although by the fluorine tests the skull and the jaw were truly contemporary, there was also clear evidence that the animal teeth and bones supposedly found with them were of a quite different age. It was hardly surprising that this announcement led to a revival of speculation about the true nature of the Piltdown skull and jaw, and among those who developed a major interest were Le Gros Clark of Oxford and his associate, J. S. Weiner.

These two scientists approached Oakley, who by that time had become the officer responsible for Physical Anthropology in the British Museum of Natural History, thus having the Piltdown skull in his care. He agreed that a much more detailed study ought to be carried out and although both Le Gros Clark and Oakley were collaborators, the main task of making the examination fell on the shoulders of young Dr. Weiner.

Early in this task, and working with the original specimens, which few before him had been allowed to look at in any detail, he was struck by the peculiar flat wear of the crowns of the molar teeth. Examining this in detail with a high-powered lens, he found that it was due to scratches that looked remarkably as though they had resulted from filing with a metal file, and not at all like ordinary wear following mastication of hard food. Weiner communicated his views to his two colleagues, and the investigation was intensified. New fluorine tests were run on the skull and the mandible, and since techniques had, by this time, very greatly improved, Oakley was able to show that the skull had in fact a greater amount of fluorine than the jaw, which appeared to be, to all intents and purposes, completely fresh bone.

Again tests were intensified, and it was then found that the ochrous color of the specimens was due to the presence of paint and coloring materials. Indeed, in a short time, it became apparent that the famous Piltdown human remains could only be explained by regarding them as a forgery and a hoax which had been perpetrated upon the scientists of the 1910–1914 period.

The story of the uncovering of this hoax has been the subject of several books, but it seems likely that the last word on the subject has not yet been written. There can be no doubt at all that at least one of the persons involved in making the forgeries must have had considerable knowledge of chemistry as well as some training in geology and human anatomy. The perpetrators also must have had access to fossil bones from outside Great Britain, since some of the

154

animal fossils "planted" with the skull and jaw, at the site, came from places like Malta and North Africa.

One of the tragedies that had resulted from the over-long acceptance of this wicked deception was that it had clouded the views of many scientists when it came to their examination and appraisal of other fossil human remains.

A fossil human mandible which had been found *in situ* at Kanam in Kenya in 1931 and published in 1932 had been rejected completely by some, and for a few others been placed in the "suspense account," simply because it had many affinities with the genus *Homo,* and yet came from deposits of very early Pleistocene age, and so was probably contemporary with the supposed Piltdown man. So long as the false evidence of the Piltdown find dominated the scene, such an interpretation seemed impossible and many maintained that the specimen from Kanam must be re-garded as that of a more recent hominid which had fallen down a crack, to become embedded in these Early Pleis-tocene deposits.

In the same way, the conclusions drawn from the Pilt-down forgery undoubtedly played a part in causing many people to reject the evidence of the Australopithecines that had been found by Dart and Broom in South Africa. It was argued that if, by the beginning of the Pleistocene, or even at the end of the Pliocene (which is where some people placed the Piltdown find), man had had a brain of approx-imately modern size but associated with an almost ape-like mandible, it was impossible to accept that the Australo-pithecines, with such very small brains, could be man's im-mediate predecessors, especially since their teeth were even

155

more like those of man than were the Piltdown teeth. Demonstrating that the Piltdown specimens were not genuine, but had been deliberately faked to deceive scientists into drawing faulty conclusions, served to clear the air considerably in respect of man's origin.

Throughout this decade, scientific thought was still dominated by the views of the late Weidenreich who had strongly advocated the theory that *Homo sapiens* was a direct descendant of *Homo erectus,* and that in turn, *Homo erectus* was derived from the Australopithecines. Many leading European and American scientists followed in Weidenreich's footsteps and propagated this view, so that it rapidly found its way into nearly every textbook. To complete the sequence, these scientists expressed the view that the Australopithecines, in their turn, were the direct, relatively recent descendants of a chimpanzee-like creature which had lived in the trees in Middle Pliocene times.

If one of the major discoveries of the decade we are now dealing with was the finding of the proof that the Piltdown skull was a forgery, the second most important discovery was of a different nature, and one which came almost at the end of the period — in July, 1959. Ever since 1931 Leakey and his colleagues had recorded the fact that there were numerous simple tools, of a culture more primitive than even the earliest stages of the hand-axe culture, to be found in Bed I at Olduvai Gorge in Tanzania. At that time, most Palaeontologists regarded Bed I at Olduvai as starting in the Middle Pleistocene; even so, the discovery and acceptance of these tools belonging to a pre-hand-axe culture had prepared scientists for the discovery at the same site, of some primitive type of hominid, responsible for making them.

In South Africa no acceptable finds of stone tools had been made in direct association with the Australopithecines but at the Third Pan-African Congress on Prehistory in 1956, Dart had maintained that he could prove that *Australopithecus africanus* had made a variety of tools and weapons from bones and teeth. This view was not widely accepted.

In 1959, Mrs. Leakey, working at Olduvai with her husband at Site FLK I near the junction of the main and the side gorges, discovered a fragment of temporal bone and two teeth of a large hominid. Excavations soon revealed a nearly complete, but broken up, skull of a creature which in its morphology was clearly a member of the Australopithecines. Unlike any previous discoveries of this subfamily of man, however, the new Australopithecine at Olduvai, which was first named *"Zinjanthropus,"* was discovered in direct association with hundreds of stone tools and bones of extinct animals, all lying on a sealed "living floor." In the absence of any evidence of some other contemporary hominid, it was a reasonably logical conclusion that *"Zinjanthropus"* represented the type of hominid that had made the tools found with him.

This could, of course, only be regarded as a hypothesis, but unfortunately many scientists immediately made pronouncements that went far beyond what was justified by the evidence. Some even stated in writing that the discovery of *"Zinjanthropus,"* in association with stone tools of the Oldowan culture, *proved* that the Australopithecines of

157

South Africa had been tool makers. It would have been just as logical to say that because it has been demonstrated that United States technicians can make a rocket which will soft-land on the moon, the Australian aborigines can also do so!

Let us for the moment leave this particular controversy and return to consider briefly the nature of *"Zinjanthropus."* The find consisted, as was stated above. of a very nearly complete skull with the greater part of the face and all the teeth well preserved. It was the skull of an individual who had died just at the time when its third molars were coming into wear, thus suggesting an age comparable to a youth of about eighteen today. The most noticeable feature of the skull was the extraordinary, well developed, bony crest, running along the mid-line at the top of the skull towards the back, a feature to be seen in some gorillas and chimpanzees, as well as some baboons and carnivores, and was clearly to be regarded as having a functional character, linked with the development of immense masticatory muscles. That such muscles had been necessary for *"Zinjanthropus"* was shown by the extraordinary size of the molar and premolar teeth and the massiveness of the bones of the face in which they are implanted. A similar situation had already been noted in South Africa, in specimens of *Paranthropus crassidens.*

In his preliminary report, Leakey summarized twenty characters that he had noted in studying the skull, stressing that some of them linked it with *Australopithecus africanus,* others with *Paranthropus crassidens,* while there were also a number of features which clearly differed from both of these, which is why he gave it a new name. He stressed, too, that its brain must have been small, and he guessed that the figure would prove to be around 600 cc.

At this point in our story, we must take note of the fact that the definition of the word "man" which was current at this time (1959) was "man begins at that stage of primate evolution when the creature begins to make tools to a set and regular pattern." The tools found with *"Zinjanthropus"* were clearly made "to a set and regular pattern" and although the morphology of the skull was clearly that of an Australopithecine, various people, including Leakey himself, suggested that we must, on the available evidence, now treat *"Zinjanthropus"* as a "man by definition."

Before six months had passed, however, Leakey and his party had made another vitally important discovery which completely altered the above interpretation concerning the significance of *"Zinjanthropus."* Leakey's son Jonathan, working with his parents early in 1960, found part of the jaw of a sabre-tooth tiger, and when following up this evidence, first uncovered some teeth, then parts of a jaw, and then skull fragments and some other bones of a fossil manlike creature.

After the preliminary examination of these specimens, found in the same geological level as *"Zinjanthropus,"* Leakey announced that he was not prepared, at this stage, to give them a scientific name, but that he considered that they clearly represented a creature which was "much closer to man as we know him today" than any Australopithecine, and might well turn out to be *Homo.* Further evidence was needed. Leakey also stressed that in view of this new discovery it was no longer justifiable to assume, as he had earlier, that *"Zinjanthropus"* made the tools found with him. Instead, three alternatives now had to be faced: (a) that the new hominid, who was more like man today, was the toolmaker, not *"Zinjanthropus;"* or (b) that *"Zinjanthropus"* was the tool-maker notwithstanding the presence of another contemporary hominid; or (c) that both might have made the primitive tools that occur in Bed I.

This tentative view was widely discussed, but few scientists found themselves able to accept the possibility of two co-existent extinct man-like creatures in the Lower Pleistocene at Olduvai. They therefore maintained, without any sound evidence in their support, that the new fossil represented no more than an unusual variation of *"Zinjanthropus."*

Thus, by the end of the decade under review the whole trend of modern thought concerning the evolution of man had been rudely shattered. On the one hand, the long cherished Piltdown discovery had been shown to be fraudulent; on the other hand, evidence had been adduced but not yet widely accepted, that it was possible to have more than one type of hominid co-existing in the early parts of the Pleistocene, and that one of these was clearly heading in the direction of man today. We shall discuss this further in the last chapter.

In addition to these major discoveries of the decade, much other important information relating to early man and his cousins was being accumulated, most of it in the continent of Africa.

In 1951, Le Gros Clark and Leakey published a monograph dealing with the fossil Miocene primates from East

Africa, the first of which had been discovered as far back as 1927 by Dr. H. L. Gorden. The first publication concerning these had appeared in 1932 as a report written by Dr. A. T. Hopwood. From 1932 to 1950 a vast number of new finds of Miocene primates had been made, but not described in any detail. In their monograph on these, the authors concentrated mainly on the genera *Proconsul* and *Limnopithecus,* treating both as members of the Pongidae. They did suggest at that time, however, that the three species of the genus *Proconsul* which they recognized exhibited in a number of their morphological characters, features which *possibly* indicated that they might represent the common ancestor of the pongids and hominids. They stressed, too, that although retaining them in the Family Pongidae, they regarded them as less like typical pongids than even the Dryopithecines, a group of extinct apes found in Europe. In particular, in respect of the backward divergence of the mandible and maxillae, the smooth rounded contour of the frontal bones from the nasion backwards, and the rectangular shape of the orbits, these *Proconsul* species recalled hominids.

This view that *Proconsul* might perhaps be an early Miocene ancestor of the Hominidae was somewhat strengthened, at the time, by the fact that no contemporary higher primates, showing some of the more typical pongid characters, had been found in Lower Miocene deposits. For example, although a specimen of *Dryopithecus* of the Middle Miocene of Europe exhibited a typical "simian shelf" and molar and pre-molar tooth rows converging backwards, no primates exhibiting these charac-

161

ters had yet been found contemporary with *Proconsul* in Kenya.

In their monograph, Le Gros Clark and Leakey also described a small fragment of maxilla which very clearly did not fit into the pattern of the *Proconsul* group of primates. As a temporary measure they referred it to the Asiatic Upper Miocene genus *Sivapithecus,* giving it a new specific name *africanus.* They stressed that in certain of its dental characters — in particular the reduction of the cingulum and the shape of the cusps of the molar teeth — this primate was more akin to the Hominidae than any other of their specimens. As we shall see in the next chapter, this specimen eventually proved to represent a true member of the Hominidae, but this was only after additional discoveries had been made which increased our overall knowledge.

Another important discovery during this decade was made in 1953, when Dr. Ronald Singer and Mr. K. Jolly of the University of Cape Town were exploring the exposures at Elandsfontein Farm, ten miles south-west of Hopefield. There they discovered remains of a fossilized human skull with an extensive fossil mammalian fauna and some stone tools. The finding of this skull was of very considerable interest and importance for it clearly resembled the so-called "Rhodesian man" skull from Broken Hill, which had been found in 1921. The Saldanha skull thus indicates a widespread diffusion of this type of hominid in Africa during the Upper Pleistocene. Scientific opinion today generally regards the Saldanha skull and the Rhodesian skull as representing an extinct race of *Homo sapiens* referred to as *Homo sapiens rhodesiensis.*

North Africa was also yielding useful new data. In 1954, Biberson of Algeria, while engaged in excavations at Sidi Abderrahman, found two fragments of a hominid mandible in a subsidiary deposit known as the Littoriana Cave. While these specimens clearly resembled the genus *Homo,* they probably provide insufficient evidence upon which to justify the suggestion (which has been made by Professor Arambourg,) that they are additional examples of a North African variant of *Homo erectus.* That they have similarities, at least at the generic level, with the specimens which he found at Ternifine, is not seriously in doubt.

The gravel pit at Ternifine had been known to be rich in extinct fauna for a very large number of years, and it had also been known to yield excellent Acheulean-type hand axes. Following the meeting of the Second Pan-African Congress in Algeria in 1952, Arambourg decided to carry out new major excavations at the Ternifine site. This decision was amply rewarded by the discovery of parts of three mandibles and a single parietal of an extinct fossil hominid. In due course, Arambourg described these specimens as representing a new genus of man, to which he gave the generic name of *Atlanthropus.* At the same time, he expressed the view that the specimens were closely comparable to *Homo erectus,* from China and Java.

Most contemporary scientists rejected the new name but agreed that there was no doubt that the specimens represented the genus *Homo.* The problem was to decide what specific identification should be assigned to this material. Most anatomists now refer the Ternifine specimens to a North African variant of *Homo erectus,* but with little justi-

163

fication, since the most diagnostic parts of the species *erectus* are the frontal bone, the temporal bones and the occipital. None of these parts are preserved in the Ternifine collection. It seems wiser, at the moment, to refer to the material as *Homo sp. indet.**

Another discovery in Africa was that of a mandible found in "Smugglers Cave," on the coast of Morocco, about eleven miles from Rabat in 1958. According to the finder, it was associated with artifacts of an Upper Acheulean type. It has been suggested by Vallois that this specimen represented a primitive proto-*Homo sapiens*, comparable to the specimens from Steinheim and Montmaurin, but until it has been described in greater detail it is hard to assess its true affinities.

The year 1958 takes us back again to South Africa where Dart announced the discovery of the first fragment of *Australopithecus* so far recovered from the so-called "pink breccia" at the Makapan site. It consisted of the greater part of a skull and face of an *Australopithecus africanus,* and is probably the best preserved specimen found so far at Makapan. Other less complete Australopithecine specimens were also found at Makapan in the years 1958—59.

This review of the progress of the discovery of human remains during the period 1950—1959 shows very clearly how the whole focus of research in the field of human palaeontology had shifted to the African continent. This was indeed fortunate for, as we saw in the *Introduction,* Darwin had prophesied, nearly 100 years before, that Africa

---

* *sp. indet.,* means "of a species at present not identified."

would yield important evidence of human evolution. Now that work was finally being carried out in the right continent, important results were appearing at an ever accelerating pace.

In 1935 von Koenigswald had published a note concerning a few gigantic fossil teeth from China under the name of *Gigantopithecus blacki,* but nothing further which would throw light on this creature was found until 1956, when work was carried out under the direction of Dr. W. C. Pei in a cave at Kwangsi. Two mandibles and some isolated teeth were then recovered which undoubtedly belonged to *Gigantopithecus.* In the next season, 1957–58, another mandible was recovered. The discovery of these three mandibles and their publication by Pei in 1957 and 1958 respectively, led to considerable controversy. Some maintained that the nearly complete mandibles which had now been found, exhibited such patently pongid characters that they must be ranked with the Pongidae. Others, however, pointed to the complete absence of other fundamental pongid characters and maintained that *Gigantopithecus* ought, therefore, to be regarded as a very aberrant side branch of the Hominidae. One or two people (who had not had the privilege of examining casts of the mandible) even went so far as to suggest that *Gigantopithecus* might perhaps be a representative of the Australopithecinae, from which, however, it differs in almost every respect except size.

The mandibles are of the very greatest interest and Leakey and Woo, after recent discussions, have come to the conclusion that *Gigantopithecus* is in fact, neither a hominid nor a pongid, but like *Oreopithecus,* a member of that strange and distinct Family now widely recognized as the Oreopithecidae. In just the same way that there was a clash of opinion as to whether *Oreopithecus* was a pongid or a hominid and has proved to be neither, so this gigantic cave-dwelling primate from China may well be regarded as the final end-product, prior to extinction, of the aberrant Family of higher primates represented in the Oligocene by *Apidium,* in the Miocene and Pliocene by *Oreopithecus,* and finally in the Pleistocene of the Far East by *Gigantopithecus.*

In 1955 John Wymer of Reading, England, carried out new excavations at the Swanscombe gravel pit, where the original Swanscombe specimens had been found, and recovered a right parietal bone which certainly belongs to the same individual as the two earlier specimens. Following this discovery, a new study was published in 1964. The general consensus of opinion today is that the Swanscombe skull represents an early ancestral stage of *Homo sapiens,* comparable to the Steinheim skull from Germany and the Fontéchevade skulls from France, as well as the Kanjera skulls from Kenya. Some authorities however, including Arambourg, do not accept this reading of the evidence and maintain that the Swanscombe skull fragments represent *Homo erectus.*

In 1959 some fragments of a skull and teeth were found in Israel just south of the Sea of Galilee, near the west bank of the Jordan where it flows out of Galilee. These specimens are too fragmentary to warrant any identification other than being referred to *Homo sp. indet.* Unfortunately they have nevertheless been described by one author as representing a near-eastern *Homo erectus,* and by another as representing a near-eastern Australopithecine, while in one recent textbook these scanty specimens have, in two successive chapters, been used as evidence for the presence of both *Australopithecus* and *Homo erectus* in Israel!

Leakey and Tobias examing "Zinjanthropus" remains.

PART III

THE PRESENT

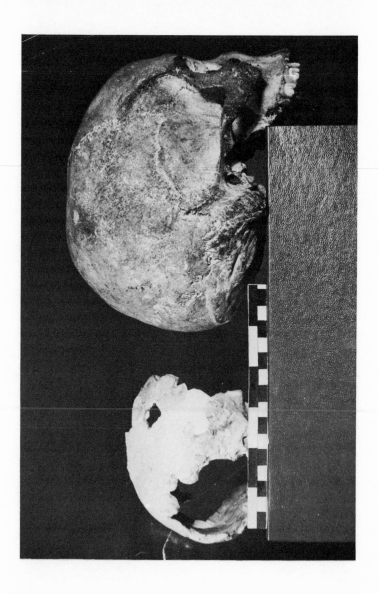

Homo habilis female skull cap compared with skull of modern man.

CHAPTER XIII
1960—1968

The last decade of our review has not yet come to an end, but with eight years already completed, it is possible to see that the speed of discovery in matters relating to human evolution has again been very greatly accelerated. It must not, however, be imagined that we are anywhere near final knowledge about our ancestry, but certainly a great deal has become much clearer during the past few years.

As in the previous decade, by far the most important discoveries have come from the continent of Africa, but there have been some exciting finds in Europe and in Asia as well. There are also signs that studies in America are being directed towards the search for a much earlier stage of human invasion of that continent than had been thought possible until recently. Indeed, there are some who believe that a primitive hominid, possibly even some form of *Homo erectus,* may have crossed into the Americas during the Middle Pleistocene at the same time as the ancestors of the big-horned sheep, the bison, the mountain goat and other Asiatic mammals which certainly wandered across the land bridge where the Bering Straits now exist.

In 1960 Dr. Yves Coppens of Paris and his wife, who

were conducting palaeontological research near Lake Tchad in North Africa found a very weathered frontal and facial fragment of a fossil hominid which they announced as an Australopithecine. Subsequently it was named *Tchadanthropus uxoris*.

For one of the more important discoveries during the decade, we return once more to Olduvai Gorge where in December, 1960, the greater part of a cranium of a fossil hominid was discovered at Site LLK in Bed II. In the preliminary announcement, it was suggested that this skull might perhaps be regarded as representing one of the makers of the Chellean stage of culture, since it was found at the same geological horizon and not very distant laterally from specimens which had been attributed, in 1951, to Stage III of the Chellean culture of East Africa.

The cranium is relatively complete but lacks face and mandible. It carries a frontal torus of an exaggerated size, far greater than that seen in any specimen of *Homo erectus* from the Far East, and even more massive than the brow ridges of Rhodesian man. In its main morphology including that of the occipital and temporal bones, this specimen is closely similar to *Homo erectus* from the Far East. Whether or not it was associated with a mandible like those from Ternifine is not yet clear, but there can be no doubt that it should be referred to the genus and species of *Homo erectus,* since the most diagnostic features — torus, occipital and temporal bones — all conform to this type.

Two major discoveries were made in Africa during the period under review that have altered the whole scientific attitude to the progress of man's evolution from more primitive stages. The first of these consisted of additional specimens supporting the find reported in the last chapter of a more advanced hominid than *"Zinjanthropus"* who was contemporary with the Australopithecines in the Lower Pleistocene. The second was the proof that the fossil primate referred to in the last chapter as *Sivapithecus africanus* was, in fact, a representative of a fully established Family of the Hominidae which was already developing in East Africa from the Lower to Upper Miocene times.

In 1962, at a site known as MNK II in Olduvai Gorge, parts of a skull, parts of the upper jaw and a mandible of a young adult hominid were found within the Middle Pleistocene deposits of Bed II. Both in respect of the morphology of the skull and of the jaw and teeth, there could be no doubt that this specimen represented the same type of hominid as that found at FLK NNI in 1960. It was no longer necessary to leave this new hominid unnamed. Leakey therefore, in conjunction with Professor Philip Tobias and Dr. John Napier, published a long note in *Nature* describing it as *Homo habilis*. Before describing the new species, they redefined the genus *Homo,* rejecting as unscientific the character of "brain size" as a diagnostic feature of *Homo*. They stressed, rather, the morphology of the back of the skull, of the vault and of the teeth. Napier was also able to show that the hand and foot bones exhibited characters strongly recalling those of man today.

The announcement that *Homo habilis* lived side by side with *"Zinjanthropus"* in East Africa was not readily considered valid by most scientists. Many, led by Le Gros

Clark and Robinson, maintained that what had been named *Homo habilis* was no more than a variant of *Australopithecus*. In particular, they tried to identify it with *Australopithecus africanus,* the so-called gracile species of Australopithecines. Leakey countered this suggestion by publishing photographs showing both the skull morphology of *Homo habilis* as well as the morphology of the mandibular arcade, viewed side by side with a variety of other hominid forms. Few, thereafter, doubted the validity of *Homo habilis,* since the contrasts were very striking. Tobias, moreover, published evidence on the brain morphology and teeth, which again stressed the *Homo* status of this new fossil.

In 1967, additional finds representing *Homo habilis* were made by the U.S.A. party of the International Expedition to the Omo Valley in Ethiopia. Here too, *habilis* was contemporary with Australopithecines. Thus, in a matter of only a few years, it became established that hominids who belonged to the same genus as ourselves, and with a morphology remarkably like man today, had developed in East Africa during the Lower and Middle Pleistocene side by side with other hominid forms.

Another find having a major bearing on human evolution was the discovery, at Fort Ternan, of *Kenyapithecus wickeri*. In the first scientific paper describing this find, Leakey suggested a conservative age of "Early Pliocene." He did not, moreover, go so far as to suggest that the specimen represented a member of the Family Hominidae. He did, on the other hand, draw attention to two important facts: first, that there was a considerable similarity between

Kenyapithecus wickeri and *Ramapithecus brevirostris* from India, and secondly, that both exhibited a number of characters more like those of hominids than pongids.

Here it is necessary to digress for a moment and consider the question of *Ramapithecus*. The type specimen was found by G. Edward Lewis of Yale in 1936, and was among a number of specimens of fossil primates which he took back to the United States from an expedition to the Siwalik Hills in India. At the outset, in his preliminary report, Lewis stressed the hominid resemblances of his *Ramapithecus* specimen, but his colleagues and his seniors would not accept his view, and it was categorically stated that Lewis must be wrong, and that the fossil was nothing more than another variant of the pongids. When Leakey published *Kenyapithecus wickeri* in 1962 and drew attention to its resemblances to *Ramapithecus,* Elwyn Simons of Yale re-examined Lewis's original specimen and stated that he had little doubt that it represented a primitive member of the Hominidae.

Dealing with the discovery of *Kenyapithecus wickeri,* Leakey had also drawn attention to the similarity between this primate and the specimen provisionally described by himself and Le Gros Clark in 1951 as *Sivapithecus africanus.* He thereafter, began to re-examine all the fossil primate remains from the early Miocene beds of Rusinga and Songhor to see if he could find further evidence of the presence of some form of *Kenyapithecus* in the early Miocene deposits.

The net result of this inquiry was the publication in January, 1967, of a lengthy report in *Nature* establishing the presence of the Family Hominidae in the early Miocene deposits of Kenya, represented by parts of no less than seven individuals. The early Miocene species was called *Kenyapithecus africanus*. In the same paper, *Kenyapithecus wickeri* was shown to be an Upper Miocene representative of the Hominidae, a place which it now shares with *Ramapithecus*. Meanwhile, Elwyn Simons had suggested that some of the specimens formerly listed as belonging to the genus *Sivapithecus* were identical to *Ramapithecus,* and he suggested that the generic name of *Sivapithecus* had priority for the hominid *Ramapithecus brevirostis,* which should therefore be called *Sivapithecus.* The validity of this suggestion has yet to be fully established.

The point of importance that emerges from these discoveries is that evidence is now clearly available to show that the Family of man was already separated from the pongids, or apes, in early Miocene times. It was fully contemporary with the genus *Proconsul* which had previously been suggested as a possible common ancestor of hominids and pongids.

Linked with this discovery of true Hominidae in the early Miocene was the parallel discovery of remains of a very large extinct primate which was temporarily placed by W. Bishop and J. Allbrook in the same genus as *Proconsul.* They regarded their specimens, found at Moroto in Uganda, as representing *Proconsul major,* but this identification is not regarded as valid by most scientists. The additional finds, however, leave no doubt at all that a true large ape possessing strong affinities with the gorilla was fully evolved in the general pongid direction in the early

176

Miocene. True pongids were, therefore, clearly contemporary with members of the Hominidae and with the Miocene Hylobatidae (gibbons).

In 1963 an expedition from Olduvai went northwards to Peninj on the western shores of Lake Natron under the leadership of Richard Leakey and Glynn Isaac. Very shortly after beginning their investigation, one of the staff, Mr. K. Kamoya, discovered a magnificent mandible of the same genus and species as *"Zinjanthropus."* The deposits in which it was found were shown by their geology, fauna, and culture to be approximately of the same age as Bed II at Olduvai, that is to say, contemporary with the second *Homo habilis* specimens, referred to in the early part of this chapter. The Peninj mandible, clearly represents the same type of hominid as *"Zinjanthropus."* It is Australopithecine, and entirely distinct from the co-existing *Homo habilis.* This discovery gave us, for the first time, the mandibular structure of the Australopithecines of East Africa.

Reference has been made in the Chapter on 1930-1939 to the discovery of the Kanam mandible, which was rejected by many scientists and placed by others in the so-called "suspense account," because it did not fit in to the preconceived ideas of what early Pleistocene hominids ought to look like. In 1962 Tobias published a report on the re-examination of this specimen and indicated that its morphology was not against an. early Pleistocene age. He further stated that it exhibited resemblances with the Middle Pleistocene fossil mandible from Rabat. Since the discovery of *Homo habilis* shows a true member of the genus *Homo* in the Lower Pleistocene, it has become clear

177

that a further examination of the Kanam mandible should be carried out.

An important report, which had a considerable bearing on human evolution, was that published by Dr. Jane van Lawick-Goodall concerning two aspects of the behaviour of chimpanzees. She established that chimpanzees living under wild conditions in Tanzania today make and use a variety of very primitive tools of perishable materials. She also showed that these primates regularly hunt, kill and then eat a variety of other animals including baboons, monkeys, young pigs and bush-buck. These reports opened up a completely new vista of the possible behaviour pattern of early proto-man. Obviously if true modern pongids with brains of from 300 to 350 cc. make and use primitive tools and indulge in a certain degree of carnivorous behaviour, the possibility can no longer be excluded that members of the Family Hominidae, even back in Miocene times, may have acted in a similar manner.

It was, therefore, not a great surprise to his colleagues when Simons issued a note suggesting that the tooth wear of *Ramapithecus* and *Kenyapithecus* was suggestive of an omnivorous diet rather than a frugivorous one. A little later Leakey reported the discovery, at Fort Ternan, of bones which had been deliberately broken open by "bashing" with some blunt instrument, as well as the discovery of one stone which could have been used for this purpose. These finds were associated with *Kenyapithecus wickeri* in Upper Miocene deposits.

At Olduvai in 1963 one of Leakey's staff found a hominid skull washed out on to the surface, at a site known as

Maiko Gully. At the time it was discovered, it had been seriously damaged as a result of being trodden on by Masai cattle coming down to water at the bottom of the Gorge. In their preliminary note on this specimen published in 1962, the Leakeys suggested that it might perhaps represent *Homo habilis,* but after reconstruction had been completed and the teeth carefully examined, it became apparent that while this specimen represented a true member of the genus *Homo* rather than an Australopithecine, it had affinities more with *Homo erectus* than with *Homo habilis.* The detailed study is not complete but published information has stressed this similarity and indicates that in Bed II at Olduvai, there were three, not two, contemporary and co-developing lines of hominid evolution. One was this proto-*erectus* leading to *erectus,* another was *Homo habilis,* leading to man today, and the third, *"Zinjanthropus"* heading for extinction.

The Harvard University Expedition working in North Kenya in 1966 discovered a small fragment of a hominid humerus lying on the surface near the fossiliferous exposure of Kanapoi. The age of the Kanapoi deposit is provisionally regarded as Early Villafranchian, roughly contemporary with Kanam west, where the Kanam mandible came from. This humerus fragment was not found *in situ* and therefore cannot be established as representing a hominid of Early Villafranchian age, although that is distinctly possible. The fragment shows some resemblances to a humerus fragment from Swartkrans; but this is insufficient evidence on which to claim that it represents an Australopithecine, for the Swartkrans hominids include not only the Australopithecine

Paranthropus, but also the hominid once called *Telanthropus* and now assigned to the genus *Homo.* It is distinctly possible that the humerus from Kanapoi may one day be shown to represent the same genus and species as the Kanam mandible.

On the west side of Baringo in 1966, two fossil human discoveries were made. Mr. John Martyn, a young geologist attached to Bedford College, London, in the course of a geological research survey, discovered a human temporal bone on the surface of deposits belonging to the Chemeron formation. He regards it as probably derived from those beds, in their upper levels. If so, this temporal would be roughly contemporary with the lower part of Bed I at Olduvai. The specimen has been described in *Nature* for the time being, as *Homo sp. indet.*

In the same area, an expedition led by Richard Leakey and his wife Margaret found a human mandible and a few parts of an associated skeleton, partly deriving from and partly *in situ,* in the Kapthurin formation. Provisionally this deposit is believed to be comparable in age to the upper part of Bed IV at Olduvai. It has yielded an advanced and rather specialized industry of the Acheulean culture. For the moment this hominid mandible is simply referred to as *Homo sp. indet.,* but it is certainly of major interest.

During 1967, an International Expedition, with parties from France, the United States and Kenya, as well as from Ethiopia, conducted the first of a series of research expeditions to the Omo Valley in Southern Ethiopia, at the north end of Lake Rudolph. Preliminary reports indicate that the French party discovered a mandible of an Australopithecine as well as a tooth of *Homo habilis;* the American party, three teeth of *Homo habilis* type. The Kenya party discovered two primitive *Homo sapiens* type skulls, from deposits of a younger age than the main Omo fossiliferous series, and probably of late Middle Pleistocene age.

Leaving Africa, we turn briefly to the discoveries in other continents. The most important find during the eight year period we are covering was the discovery of an occipital bone at the important prehistoric site at Vértesszöllös in Hungary by Professor Laszlo Vértes. It was associated with a primitive culture and a fauna of Middle Pleistocene age. Although the occipital was first placed on record as having *Homo erectus* affinities, further investigation shows clearly that its real similarity lies with the Swanscombe and Steinheim skulls; in other words, it represents a primitive proto-*Homo sapiens.*

In China, Woo and Pei announced the discovery of the Lantien skull which has resemblances to the *Homo erectus* skulls from Choukoutien. Detailed reports are not yet available.

In Borneo, Dr. Tom Harrison announced the discovery of a juvenile skull which has been dated by Carbon 14 tests of the associated charcoal as approximately 40,000 years old. This skull is that of a true *Homo sapiens* and is thus, for the moment, the oldest skull of this type to be dated by the Carbon 14 process.

181

EPILOGUE

Charles Darwin's prophecy is coming true. More and more evidence is accumulating which points to the African continent, and particularly the East/Central African region, as the cradle of the Family Hominidae, to which all mankind, living and extinct, belongs.

This fact should not allow scientists to reduce their efforts to search for man's past elsewhere in the world, because the story of man's slow and gradual evolution to the status which we have today is not all to be found in Africa. A vast amount of work must still be done in Africa, but also in other lands, before we can hope for a complete picture.

At the moment all the available evidence points clearly to a separation of the Pongidae, or Apes, from the Hominidae, or Family of Man, in Early Miocene times in Africa, with still earlier ancestral stages to be found in the Oligocene beds of the Fayoum in Egypt. There can be no doubt that this Fayoum region played a very important part, some forty million years ago, as a center of evolution of hominids and of many other mammals. It is possible that this "center" extended across into what is now the Sinai Desert and Arabia as a whole. A vast amount of exploration must be done in this region. Simons of Yale, has been working in the Fayoum for some time but the political situation, at the moment, is not very favorable for continuing this study.

The fact that members of the family Hominidae, represented by *Ramapithecus brevirostris,* have been found in the Siwalik Hills of India is even more important to our consideration of where work needs to be carried out. These discoveries point to a movement out of Africa into Central Asia during Middle and Upper Miocene times by a primate stock which was already fully hominid. We must therefore ask ourselves the following questions. Was it this branch of the hominid Family which eventually evolved into the Far Eastern *Homo erectus* represented by Java and Pekin Man? Were these forms perhaps the result of some sort of evolution in Asia, parallel to the development in Africa of *Homo habilis* as well as the African variety of *Homo erectus?* These possibilities cannot be ignored.

Another possibility is that the *Ramapithecus* branch of the Hominidae eventually died out completely and that it was, rather, the descendants of the East African *Kenyapithecus* branch of the Hominidae that alone evolved into the genus *Homo,* as represented both by *Homo habilis* and *Homo erectus.* If so, then it would seem that a *Homo erectus* branch moved slowly out of Africa and into the Far East, in the Early and Middle Pleistocene.

No matter which theory we prefer there is no doubt now that further investigation is required. Too much surface collecting has been carried out in the Siwaliks with too little detailed investigation by excavation. It is important to remember that between the geographic range of *Kenyapithecus* and *Ramapithecus* and between the geographic range of the African *Homo erectus* and the Far Eastern equivalent, there are immense gaps. Some of these will be filled, sooner or later, in Israel. Other intermediate sites lie buried in the Arabian peninsulas and in places like Baluchistan and Afghanistan.

We have seen that scientists at present group the original *Homo erectus* fossil types found in the Far East with the supposed *Homo erectus* type of Africa, such as the specimens from LLK II at Olduvai and Ternifine in Algeria. We have no positive proof, however, that this is true. It may well be that these two branches separated much further back in time, before becoming true examples of *Homo*.

Another possibility that we cannot ignore is that what we call *Homo erectus* did evolve somewhere in Asia, possibly from *Ramapithecus* stock as suggested above, and that there was a reverse migration into Africa at a time when *Homo habilis* was evolving independently in that continent.

The available evidence very strongly suggests that it was *Homo habilis* and not *Homo erectus* who was the direct ancestor of man as we know him today. This view destroys the theory, so long prevalent, that creatures like Peking Man and Java Man were our direct ancestors.

Much closer study must be given to the question of whether different species of the genus *Homo* may have been capable of interbreeding. Theoretically, and by definition, distinct species like *Homo erectus* and *Homo habilis* should have been incapable of fertile crossing. Nevertheless, we know that under the specialized conditions of domestication, fertile crosses are sometimes possible between what, in the wild state, are distinct species. Man, by his very nature, is self-domesticated, and he may therefore have been affected by this rule.

There are so many gaps in the story of human evolution still waiting to be filled that many more intensive studies are needed. People who are only prepared to devote a few months to such research and then return to more lucrative and comfortable work in Universities are not suitable for this work. A number of really dedicated, adequately trained scientists — men and women — who are prepared to give up other work and devote many years to hard and often uncomfortable situations in Africa, Asia, Europe, and even America, are urgently needed. They must truly dedicate themselves to the search for man's past for long periods if they want to achieve something worthwhile. America, as just mentioned, can no longer be ignored in such a programme. When the senior author was a student, just after World War I, it was commonly believed that man had not reached the American continent before about 3,000 B.C. This date has already been pushed back, and widely accepted dates for the arrival of man in the United States range around 18,000 B.C. It must be remembered that students of geomorphology and zoology have now shown that certain elements of the living American fauna — including bison, mountain sheep and mountain goat and some of the now extinct animals like the true elephant — moved into America during the Pleistocene, at a time when the Bering Straits area comprised a major land bridge. It is known that Asia was inhabited at that time by a sparse population of *Homo erectus* people. Is it really likely that these hominids would not have crossed this land bridge as they followed the

185

animals they hunted? Surely it is more probable that they did so in small numbers, and that sooner or later their remains and their culture will be found in America.

There are still immense gaps in our knowledge of the beginnings of *Homo sapiens*. There are examples of true *Homo sapiens* dating back around 28,000 — 30,000 years. A number of examples which are regarded as proto-*Homo sapiens* such as those from Swanscombe, Steinheim, Kanjera and Fontechevade are known, and these date back 100,000 years or more. There is a long interval of time separating proto-*Homo sapiens* from *Homo habilis*. Obviously there is an immense field to study before these gaps can be bridged. It will require endless patience, much time and adequate financial backing to solve all these problems, but there is no doubt at all that the task will be worthwhile, and that those who undertake it will achieve something they will never regret. They will be amply rewarded by knowing that they have added to the overall knowledge of how man became man.

POSTCRIPT

Since the typescript of this book was sent to the printers a few important new discoveries have been announced as follows:

a. In the United States, Leakey and his colleagues Miss Ruth De Ette Simpson and Dr. Tom Clements have reported, in *Science,* the results of an excavation carried out in an old alluvial fan at the foot of the Calico Mountains near Yermo, Southern California.

Work was carried out here for four seasons, and as a result more than 160 specimens, which Leakey and his colleagues regard as unquestionably human artifacts, were found *in situ* in an area of less than 25 x 25 feet. Any single one of these specimens, found alone, might possibly be explained as having been produced under natural conditions. When found in quantity and in such concentration as at Calico this explanation is not reasonable. They can only be regarded as of human origin and thus represent the oldest known cultural material anywhere in the New World, since the deposit is dated, by geologists, as probably between 35,000 and 100,000 years with 60,000 − 80,000 years as the most likely date.

A number of American archaeologists who have knowledge of primitive cultures in Africa, Asia and

Europe support Leakey and his colleagues' interpretation of these specimens as being of human origin, as do some British and French archaeologists. Some American pre-historians however, are sceptical at present, and prefer to interpret the finds as purely natural.

b. Dr. Elwyn Simons of Yale University has recently published a preliminary report, in *Science,* announcing the discovery of a skull and mandible of primitive higher primate form from the Oligocene deposits in the Fayoum. He regards the new specimen as belonging to the genus and species previously named by him *Aegyptopithecus zeuxis,* on the basis of earlier fragmentary material. The evidence now available makes it seem possible that *Aegyptopithecus zeuxis* may represent a common ancestor (in Oligocene times) of the subsequent Pongidae (including *Proconsul*) and of the earliest Hominidae such as *Kenyapithecus.*

c. Dr. L. S. B. Leakey has reported, in *Nature,* the discovery of a new mandible of *Kenyapithecus africanus* from Rusinga Island. This has been compared with previous material of this genus and species and confirms Leakey's earlier finds that this is a primitive genus of the Hominidae.

d. Leakey reported, in *Nature,* the discovery of a lump of lava with battered edges in direct association with broken limb bones and skulls of extinct antelope in Upper Miocene deposits at Fort Ternan, Kenya. This is the site where fossil remains of *Kenyapithecus wickeri* were earlier discovered. The new evidence, therefore,

indicates that Upper Miocene hominids were breaking open bones and skulls to obtain marrow and brains.

e. Leakey has reported, in *Nature,* the presence of an Oreopithecid and also a representative of the genus *Dryopithecus,* from Fort Ternan, Kenya.

f. Dr. Gupta of India and Elwyn Simons of Yale have reported the discovery of a mandible of an early representative of *Gigantopithecus,* from Pliocene deposits in India.

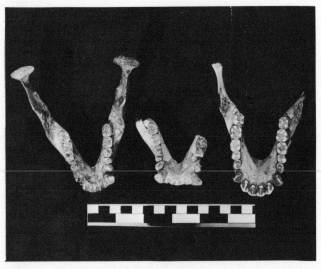

Mandible (center) of *Kenyapithecus africanus* compared with chimpanzee (right) and *Proconsul* (left).

189

PART IV

SELECTED PRINTS

ILLUSTRATING
THE DISCOVERERS
AND THEIR DISCOVERIES

Alfred Russel Wallace

193

Jacques Boucher de Perthes

Jean B. de Lamark

Thomas Henry Huxley

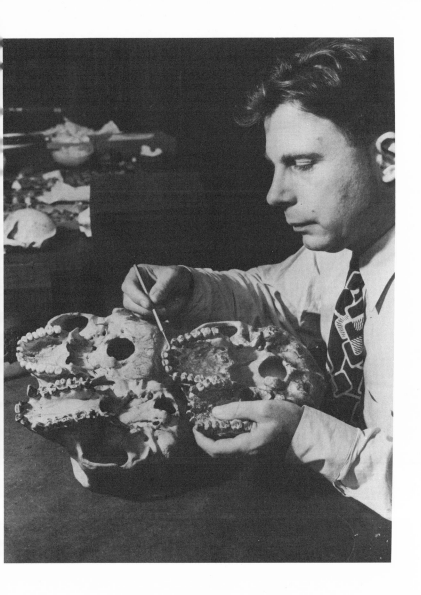

G.H.R. von Koenigswald demonstrates a reconstruction of what he once called *"Pithecanthropus robustus."* At that time he believed it was distinct from *Homo (Pithecanthropus) erectus* and also older. This is no longer accepted.

Mr. T. O. Barlow, Prof. G. Ellot Smith, Mr. Charles Dawson, Dr. Arthur Smith Woodward (back row) and Dr. A. S. Underwood, Mr. W. P. Pycraft and Sir Ray Lankester (front row) watch Prof. Arthur Keith measure the Piltdown skull.

At the right a workman stands at the spot where the original Piltdown skull fragments were alleged to have been found.

Robert Broom

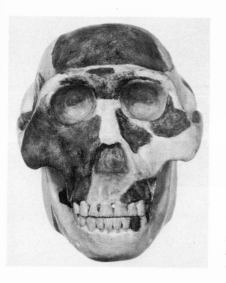

An early attempt to reconstruct
an Australopithecine based upon a variety of fragments.

197

Franz Weidenreich

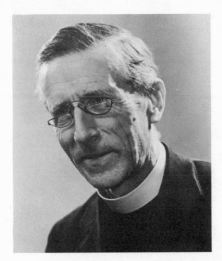

Father Pierre Teilhard
de Chardin

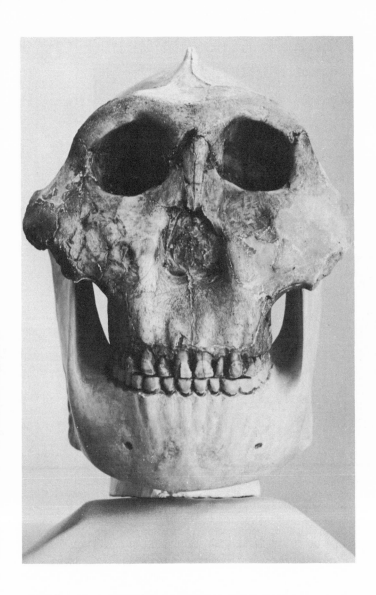

"Zinjanthropus" skull and mandible as reconstructed by Tobias. Large molars and premolars; bony ridge at the top of the skull for anchoring massive jaw muscles may indicate vegetarian diet.

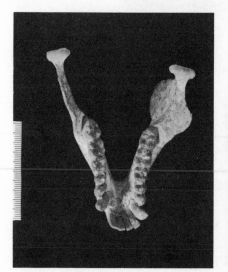

Three views of the *Proconsul africanus* skull and mandible found by Mrs. M. Leakey on Rusinga Island in 1948.

200

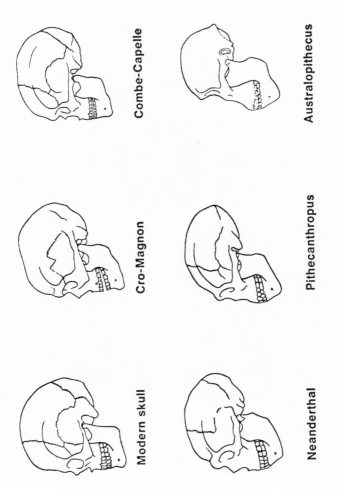

Drawings of skulls of *modern Homo sapiens* and two extinct type (Cromagnon and Combe-Capelle) to show similarities. In contrast are drawings of reconstructions of Neanderthal man, *Homo erectus* and an Australopithecine.

201

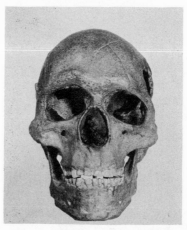

Skull found at Combe-Capelle. The individual who possessed it was a Cromagnon — one of the race which produced the cave painters and the hunters of Upper Palaeolithic times. The brain capacity equaled that of the average modern European, but the head was often a bit longer and the brow often a bit more pronounced.

WOOLLY RHINOCEROS (PAINTING)
FONT DE GAUME CAVE, FRANCE

INDEX

INDEX

INDEX

McCown, Theodore, 127

MacEnery, The Reverend John, 12

McGregor, J. H., 115

La Madeleine discovery (1864), 36-39

Magdalenian culture
  and Chancelade man, 57-60
  description, 38
  compared with Eskimos, 58-60
  Les Hoteaux, 69-70
  Mas d'Azil, 72-73

Makapan (1946), 146-147

Man, definition of
  Darwin's, 47
  Leakey, Tobias and Napier's, 173
  reason *vs.* instinct, 47
  tool maker, 4
  1870-1879, popular opinion, 46-47

Man, estimates of date of origin, 134

"The Man of China," 118-120
  See also Sinanthropus

Maiko Gully, discovery (1963), 178-179

Marston, A. T., 132, 133

Martyn, John, 180

Maschka, 75

Matrix, geological definition, xv

Meganthropus palaeojavanicus
  first discovery, 135
  Leakey on (quoted), 135
  second discovery, 140-141
  speech in, 140-141

Mercati, Michael, 4

Mindel-Riss period, 133

"Missing link"

Australopithecus africanus as, 112, 113, 114
Heidelberg man as, 79-80
Naulette mandible as, 39-40
Neanderthalers as, 54-55
original conception of, 45-46
Piltdown man as, 92, 102
Pithecanthropus erectus as, 64, 66, 114, 115-116
Sinanthropus pekinensis as, 119-120
Steinheim skull as, 130
Sterkfontein skull as, 138

Moulin Quignon discovery, (1863), 33-36

Mousterian culture
  Athlit, 127
  La Chapelle-aux-Saints, 81
  description, 38
  Ehringsdorf, 121
  La Ferrassie, 83-84
  Galilee skull, 116
  Krapina, 75-77
  Le Moustier, 82-83
  origin of, 116
  La Quina, 85-87
  Shukbah, 126
  Solutre, 40-41
  Spy, 53
  compared with Stillbay culture, 125
  technical skill, 85
  Devil's Tower Shelter, 120

Mousterian man
  overspecialized, 142-143
  reassessment called for, 143-144

Le Moustier discovery (1908)

215